C000137166

The Pan-European Ecological Network: taking stock

UNEP

Marie Bonnin, Agnès Bruszik, Ben Delbaere,
Hervé Lethier, Dominique Richard,
Sandra Rientjes, Glynis van Uden, Andrew Terry

Committee of experts for the development
of the Pan-European Ecological Network
(STRA-REP)

Nature and Environment, No. 146

Council of Europe Publishing

French edition:
Le réseau écologique paneuropéen : état d'avancement.
ISBN 978-92-871-6118-5

For a complete list of titles available in the various series, please see at the back of the book.

Cover photo: White stork *(Ciconia ciconia)* migrating, Estremadure, Spain.
© Sylvain Hellio
Cover, design and layout: Christophe Nutoni - www.instinctcreatif.com
Iconography: Biodiversity Unit, Council of Europe.

Council of Europe Publishing
F-67075 Strasbourg Cedex
http://book.coe.int

ISBN 978-92-871-6119-2
© Council of Europe, July 2007

Printed in Belgium

We should like to extend our thanks to the following institutions which have contributed to the realisation of this report:

We should like to extend our thanks to the following institutions which have contributed to the realisation of this report: European Environment Agency, European Topic Centre on Biological Diversity, World Conservation Union, European Centre for Nature Conservation, Research Institute for Development (France), Research Institute Alterra (Netherlands), Biodiversity Conservation Center (Russian Federation), EMC2I Ecosystem-Management-Conservation Consulting International.

We address special thanks to the authors of the chapters of the report:
- Ms Marie Bonnin, Research Institute for Development (IRD), C3ED-UVSQ (France),
- Ms Agnes Bruszik, Ms Sandra Rientjes, Mr. Ben Delbaere, Ms Glynis van Uden, European Centre for Nature Conservation (ECNC),
- Mr. Hervé Léthier, EMC2I Ecosystem-Management-Conservation Consulting,
- Ms Dominique Richard, European Environment Agency / European Topic Centre on Biological Diversity,
- Mr. Andrew Terry, IUCN, World Conservation Union, Regional Office for Europe.

We also express our gratitude to the institutions and national authorities which have granted a financial contribution to the drafting of this report:
- European Commission
- Ministry of the Walloon Region (Belgium)
- Ministry of Ecology and Sustainable Development (France)
- Federal Office of Environment, Forestry and Landscape (Switzerland)
- Ministry of Agriculture, Nature and Food Quality (Netherlands).

Union Européenne

Swiss Confederation

Institut de recherche
pour le développement

Agence européenne pour l'environnement

RÉGION WALLONNE

agriculture, nature
and food quality

ALTERRA
WAGENINGEN UR

ECNC
european centre for nature conservation

Summary

The information which appears on the maps and in the tables and statistics, etc, is subject to constant change and remains the responsibility of those who supplied it, and not that of the Council of Europe.

Introductory note

Following the 5th Ministerial Conference, "An Environment for Europe", the Ministers and Heads of Delegation of the region of the United Nations Economic Commission for Europe (UNECE) invited the Council of Europe and the European Centre for Nature Conservation (ECNC) to follow up and develop their activities with the intention of supporting the creation of the Pan-European Ecological Network. These activities aim particularly to identify the constituent elements of the Pan-European Ecological Network and to represent them on coherent European indicative maps as a European contribution to the creation of a global ecological network.

The present report, which contains indicative maps for several parts of Europe, stems from this mandate. It has been prepared under the aegis of the Council of Europe by the Committee of Experts for the Development of the Pan-European Ecological Network, as one of the activities in the Pan-European Biological and Landscape Diversity Strategy process.

This report is the result of the work of an Editorial Committee set up by the Committee of Experts and composed of governmental delegates from several countries participating in the Pan-European Biological and Landscape Diversity Strategy, and experts from the European Commission, the European Environment Agency and its European Topic Centre on Biological Diversity, The World Conservation Union (IUCN), the European Centre for Nature Conservation (ECNC), the French Research Institute for Development and the Dutch Research Institute Alterra (list of members in Appendix 4). The Editorial Committee met four times to co-ordinate the drafting, revision and finalisation of the Report. On these occasions, it took into account the observations and comments made by the Committee of Experts for the Development of the Pan-European Ecological Network.

The methodology used for the establishment of the report is based on the replies to a questionnaire sent to the countries participating in the PEBLDS process, on several contacts and discussions with governmental experts and on the scientific bibliography published on this topic, in particular, the work of the Council of Europe in the field of ecological networks.

The aim of the report is to inform the Ministers and Heads of delegation meeting in the 6th Ministerial Conference "Environment for Europe" in Belgrade (10-12 October 2007) on the progress of work in the constitution of the Pan-European ecological network, as a follow-up to the Resolutions of the previous Ministerial Conferences, in particular the Conferences of Sofia in 1995 and Kyiv in 2003.

Alpine gentian

Cordier-Huguet

INTRODUCTION

Oystercatchers in their biotope (D)

On 25 October 1995,

a t the Environment for Europe Ministerial Conference in Sofia, Bulgaria, 54 European Ministers of Environment endorsed the initiative to establish a Pan-European Ecological Network within the next twenty years. They envisaged the establishment of *"physical network of core areas and other appropriate measures, linked by corridors and supported by buffer zones, thus facilitating the dispersal and migration of species' (PEBLDS Strategy text)."*

In calling for the establishment of a Pan-European Ecological Network (PEEN), the Ministers were responding to the decline of biological diversity, to the loss of valuable habitats and landscapes, and to the threat this posed to the sustainable future of Europe. The Ministers' vision was to ensure ecological connectivity and resilience throughout the continent, and to provide a framework for sustainable use of land and natural resources.

Biodiversity and ecosystems contribute substantially to social and economic development and human well-being. They provide essential goods and services and the ecosystems' capacity for self-regulation is a major factor in environmental stability at the global or regional level. Europe's richness in species and natural and semi-natural habitats is significant, even if it is not the richest continent in this respect, with its estimated 2500 habitat types and 200,000 species of plants and animals. As a result of millennia of human interaction with the environment, Europe's biological diversity is intrinsically linked to the variety of landscapes, the composition and patterns of which influence the potentialities of biodiversity development and distribution, thus providing the ecological backbone of the continent (Map 1). The biological and landscape diversity of Europe are amongst the continent's most highly valued and unique heritage features.

Map 1: Potential ecological backbone of the European continent
Source: EEA/Corine Land Cover 2000 for 32 countries and JRC/Global Land Cover 2000 for 10 others)
Note: Land classes such as forests, open semi-natural and natural dry landscapes and wetlands as well as pastures and agriculture mosaics have been retained for computing an index of "green potential".

But Europe's diversity is in danger. It is threatened by the damage caused by human activities such as intensification of agriculture and forestry, land abandonment in some areas, deforestation in others, wetland drainage, the modification of coasts and rivers, mining, road construction, urbanisation and tourism The fragmentation of ecosystems and habitats as a result of transport and energy infrastructures as well as drastic land-use changes also poses a serious threat to biodiversity, particularly as this jeopardises the efficiency of protected areas, once totally isolated (Map 2a and 2b)

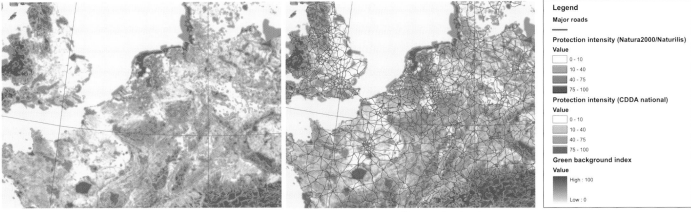

Maps 2a and 2b : Environmental context of protected areas (2a), under pressure of increasing land fragmentation by transport infrastructures (2b) in a North-Western region of Europe
Source: EEA/Corine Land Cover 2000, Natura 2000 & CDDA databases, roads by ESRI.

In fragmented habitats populations may be prevented from reaching migration and dispersal destinations, they are forced to live in habitats not large enough to enable them to survive, are unable to achieve genetic exchange or to adapt to the consequences of climate change that will force many species to migrate to new habitats. These issues affect terrestrial and marine environments alike. European oceans, seas and coasts provide enormous economic and social benefits - transportation, food, energy, recreation, tourism, that present excellent opportunities for development, if managed sustainably. However, coastal and marine habitat fragmentation, marine pollution and overexploitation of resources have continued.

The increasing pressure on natural areas and ecosystems by overexploitation and inappropriate use of natural resources constitutes a challenge to policymakers, the public and scientists alike to develop and implement strategies that will preserve European ecosystems and biodiversity sustainably.

Ecological networks with their elements of core areas, ecological corridors, buffer zones and restoration areas provide an operational model for conserving biodiversity that allows a degree of human exploitation of the landscape. Since its introduction in the 1980s the concept has been applied at the local, regional, national and supranational scale. A continent-wide ecological network was a logical next step, but for Europe this requires a shared commitment and sense of responsibility on the part of many countries. This is why in 1995 during the Environment for Europe Conference in Sofia the 54 European Environment Ministers endorsed the Pan-European Biological and Landscape Diversity Strategy (PEBLDS), which contains as one of its priorities an Action Theme to establish a Pan-European Ecological Network (PEEN) within 20 years: *"We endorse the Pan-European Biological and Landscape Diversity Strategy [...] as a framework for the conservation of biological and landscape diversity. [...] We call for the promotion of nature protection, both inside and outside protected areas, by implementing the European Ecological Network, a physical network of core areas and other appropriate measures, linked by corridors and supported by buffer zones, thus facilitating the dispersal and migration of species."* (PEBLDS Strategy text)

In 2003 the commitment of European governments to the PEEN process was reinforced in the 5th Environment for Europe Conference in Kyiv with the 'Kyiv Resolution on Biodiversity' through which heads of delegations undertook to 'halt biodiversity loss by 2010', in line with the global target adopted in 2002 by the World Summit on Sustainable Development. The establishment of a continent-wide ecological network was seen as a major contribution to halting the decline of biodiversity in Europe. Among its targets the Resolution states that:
• by 2006 the Pan-European Ecological Network will be identified in all States of the pan-European region and represented on coherent indicative European maps;
• by 2008, all core areas of the PEEN will be adequately conserved and the PEEN will give guidance to all major national, regional and international land-use and planning policies as well as to the activities of relevant economic and financial sectors.

Since the Sofia Environment for Europe Ministerial Conference in 1995 considerable progress has been made towards the establishment of PEEN. The Pan-European Ecological Network should not be seen as another policy instrument, law or directive and was never intended as such. With PEEN, the Ministers endorsed a framework for integrating existing agreements, programmes and initiatives in the field of nature conservation, land use planning and rural and urban development. Interaction and co-operation with the stakeholders involved in various forms of land use (agriculture, spatial planning, water management, infrastructure, housing, recreation, etc.) was considered to be a crucial part of the design and implementation of the PEEN, as it is in the development of any ecological network which combines top-down and bottom-up approaches. Several national, regional and transboundary initiatives have targeted and are targeting the establishment of ecological networks in Europe and thus contribute to the establishment of the Pan-European Ecological Network. However, the implementation of the PEEN targets into nature policies, land-use planning and rural and urban development in order to ensure ecological resilience, coherence and a sustainable future for Europe's biodiversity and landscapes is still a challenge for Europe.

This report gives an assessment of progress in establishing the Pan-European Ecological Network. It was produced at the request by the Council of Europe's Committee of Experts for the Establishment of the Pan-European Ecological Network and will be presented at the Environment for Europe Ministerial Conference in Belgrade (Serbia) 2007 to inform the Ministers about progress made in implementing the decisions made at the Ministerial Conferences in 1995 (Sofia) and 2003 (Kyiv).

The Pan-European Ecological Network (PEEN) aims to ensure that:

• a full range of ecosystems, habitats, species and landscapes of European importance is conserved;
• habitats are large enough to place species in a favourable conservation status;
• there are sufficient opportunities for the dispersal and migration of species;
• damaged parts of the key environmental systems are restored;
• the key environmental systems are buffered from potential threats.

D. Aubort

Polar bear eating a goose's nest (N). Both climat changes and pollution through heavy metals endanger those bears' lives, especially when they come for feeding.

It consists of four chapters:
• Chapter 1 provides an overview of the scientific background of ecological networks as well as the rationale for application on the European continent;
• Chapter 2 highlights the policy and legislative context which underpins the development of the PEEN;

• Chapter 3 shows how PEEN is progressively building up through a combination of supranational, national and regional initiatives;
• Chapter 4 draws conclusions on main achievements so far, and identifies challenges and opportunities for the future.

THE PAN-EUROPEAN ECOLOGICAL NETWORK

CHAPTER
I

Scientific background of ecological networks and
rationale for application on the European continent

*Booschplaat Natural Reserve (NL), holder of the European Diploma of
Protected Areas since 1970.*

Background of ecological networks

Scientific and political background of the ecological network concept

The concept of ecological networks was basically formulated as a response to the habitat fragmentation process. In a fragmented habitat:
• individual animals may not have access to an area holding habitats necessary for their survival;
• migratory animals may be unable to move to those areas where they would normally stay for part of the year;
• natural populations and communities may be unable to move across the landscape in response to changing environmental conditions, especially to climate change;

• genetic exchange between different local populations may be prevented;
• a patch of habitat in which a species has become locally extinct cannot easily be re-colonised by another local population of the same species (CBD, 2005).

By the end of the 19th century the nature conservation movement had already laid the foundation for the protection of scientifically, aesthetically or culturally valued natural areas through the creation of national parks and nature reserves. This continued to be the main trend in conservation until the second half of the 20th century.

❶ The scientific roots of ecological networks: new developments in conservation ecology

Island biogeography theory, developed by MacArthur and Wilson (1967), concluded that the number of species that can be found on an island is determined by the balance between the rate at which new species colonise the island and the rate at which species become extinct. This theory has been applied to "habitat islands", located in the middle of a hostile land environment. However, there has been controversy over the use of concepts from this theory within a land environment. There are limits to comparisons between these two types of islands owing to differences in timescale of the phenomena and the fact that mainland "habitat" islands are often not fully isolated. Scientists no longer use this theory to demonstrate the risks of excessive fragmentation of natural habitats.

Levins in 1969 analysed the fragmentation of natural habitats in terms of demographic and genetic processes on the scale of individuals and populations.

This is the theory of meta-populations. Meta-populations are sets of scattered populations between which there are exchanges of individuals. The theory concludes that rather than existing as stable, homogeneous populations, species are dynamic entities that are distributed unevenly across landscapes in habitats of varying quality. Local populations are vulnerable to extinction, but as long as individuals from other local populations can re-colonise the empty habitat, the meta-population can continue to survive. The connectivity of the landscape for species depends on the mobility of a species and the type of the available habitat and its configuration in the landscape. In this respect corridors are very important for certain species (van der Sluis et al., 2004). These insights led in turn to the inference that habitat fragmentation increases the vulnerability of species populations by reducing the area of habitat available to local populations and limiting the opportunities for dispersal, migration and genetic exchange.

The landscape polarisation theory, developed by Rodoman (1974), also divides the landscape between

In the 1960s nature conservation focused increasingly on the preservation of ecological values in semi-natural landscapes and habitats; this occurred especially in North-Western Europe, where the decline in biodiversity and ecosystems reached alarming levels after the Second World War. In the following decades new theories and approaches in landscape ecology, conservation biology and ecosystem science (island biogeography theory, meta-population theory and landscape polarisation theory, sink-source theory, "new" non-equilibrium paradigms – see box 1) triggered the development of new perspectives on the most effective way to protect nature and biodiversity, including the concept of ecological networks. It became clear that protected 'nature islands' alone were not sufficient to maintain biodiversity. Fragmentation and isolation of habitats and loss of ecological connectivity lead to a decline of biodiversity both within and outside protected areas. The focus of nature conservation shifted from areas of high nature concentration to the links between them and to links between nature and the human environment.

It was necessary to develop a model that would safeguard the conservation of ecosystems and biodiversity in protected areas as well as the wider landscape, while simultaneously providing a framework for the sustainable use of landscapes and natural resources.

An ecological network through its system of core areas, corridors and buffer zones was seen to provide a model that can positively influence the conditions for the survival of species populations in the fragmented natural areas and human dominated landscapes in Europe. In addition, it allows a suitable and sustainable use of natural resources through interconnectivity of its physical elements with the landscape and existing social/institutional structures' (based on SBSTTA 9).

In other words, ecological networks significantly contribute to human well-being and sustainable development.

From the 1980s onward, initiatives were developed in many countries in Europe to establish ecological networks at the local, regional, national or supranational scale (an overview of these initiatives is provided in Chapter 3, and the concept of ecological networks became increasingly prominent in national and international policy and law (an overview is provided in Chapter 2). In recent years, interest in the concept of ecological networks received an additional boost through growing awareness of the potential threat to biodiversity in Europe posed by climate change. Although it is unknown how climate change will actually affect ecosystems and how ecosystems and populations will respond to climate change, it is probable that climate change will form a threat to many species and ecosystems, especially in fragmented habitats. It will force many species and their populations to move to new habitats. Without adequate ecological connectivity, many species will be trapped in habitats that will rapidly become unsuited to their needs as the climate changes. It is generally agreed that as climate change affects protected areas, which hitherto have been the main tool for protecting

'anthropocentric core areas', 'buffer zones' and 'ecotones' on the one hand and large natural ecosystems on the other hand with transition zones. It has been the basis for e.g. the Estonian, the Lithuanian and Russian ecological networks. In these plans the relationship between human land use and the ecologically stabilising landscape functions has been emphasized.

The sink-source theory (Pulliard, 1988) shows that in heterogeneous landscapes, a habitat may act as a source for species which will colonise other close areas that are too small to maintain a viable population of this species. By hosting these new individuals and thus acting as a "sink", these areas will play a new role in the dispersal of the species population without connexion with a source (Clergeau and Désiré 1999).

The new paradigm on non-equilibrium maintains ecological systems are open and have multiple persistent states and multiple pathways of change that are driven by process. This new paradigm also recognises the importance of disturbances such as fire, floods, and hurricanes in determining ecosystem structure (McDonnell, M., 1997)

European biodiversity, conservation targets will need to be redefined in order to meet the challenges of global warming. Connectivity among protected areas will therefore have to be promoted by establishing ecological networks and avoiding fragmentation (EEA, 2005).

Functions and components of ecological networks

The ecological functions of ecological networks are to maintain ecosystem processes by:
• conserving a representative array of habitats allowing species populations access to a sufficient surface area (for foraging, the dispersal of juveniles as well as adults or the colonisation of other habitat patches);
• allowing seasonal migration, permitting genetic exchange between different local populations, allowing local populations to move away from deteriorating habitats; and also migration due to global warming;
• securing the integrity of vital environmental processes (such as periodic flooding, ecological successions).

In addition to this conservation dimension, the ecological network approach identifies appropriate opportunities within the landscape matrix for the exploitation of natural resources – agriculture, forestry, fishing, human settlements, recreation, etc.

(Bennett, 2004).

Fishermen

An ecological network model is usually applied by allocating specific functions to different areas depending on their ecological value and their natural-resource potential (Bennett, 2004). Regardless of the scale at which they apply (i.e. local, regional, national or international), almost all examples of ecological networks include some or all of the following components:
• core areas,
• corridors including stepping stones,
• buffer zones,
• restoration areas.

However, other approaches to ensure ecological connectivity are possible and are being applied in Europe. The United Kingdom applies the wider landscape approach. Emphasis in this approach is less on identifying various elements such as those listed above, and more on ensuring sufficient ecological and landscape quality over as wide a range of the territory as possible.

Figure 1: Elements of the ecological network (Bouwma *et al.*, 2002)

Core area

Landscape corridor

Core area

Stepping stone corridor

Core area

Linear corridor

Buffer zone

Restoration area

Core areas

Core areas are adequately managed (i.e. most, but not necessarily all legally protected) areas with high natural values, areas of conservation of habitats, species or landscapes. In ecological networks in Europe, core areas are zones which are of particular importance for conservation of valuable habitats, species or landscapes because they act as reservoirs for biodiversity where evolution and reproductive processes can take place.

Many of these areas have already been identified by traditional nature conservation policies, and received protection under national laws, or European or international regulations, but they may also include large unprotected areas.

The definitions of protected areas and the management rules of protected areas may vary from country to country throughout Europe, but basically the identification of core areas in different national and regional network designs developed so far is based on (see Biró *et al.*, 2006):
• legally designated areas – the different categories of internationally and nationally protected areas;
• large unfragmented habitats - research on species viability underlines the need for core areas of size and spatial configuration sufficient to enable intermingling of species;
• important hotspots for certain species based on their distribution;
• location of valuable landscapes;
• geomorphological characteristics. (ECNC, 2006, at press).

Ecological corridors

Ecological corridors are physical landscape elements or other structures (such as eco-ducts) that provide ecological connectivity and coherence. The ecological functions of corridors are to enable species dispersal, migration, foraging and reproduction.

2

Examples of ecological corridors: size and function vary widely according to species

Migration corridors
• Frogs migrate for breeding purposes over a distance of 0.01–5 km.
• Some 'coastline corridor' (at altitude) zones at either side of the coastline used by species that prefer to migrate over either land or above sea, like geese *(Anser sp.)*, storks *(Ciconia sp.)*, swallows *(Hirundo rustica)* and eels *(Anguilla anguilla)*. They migrate over a distance of 1000km- 20,000km.
• Marine corridors (underwater) enable species like dolphins *(Delphinus sp.)*, tuna *(Thunnus sp.)* and swordfish *(Xiphias gladius)* to migrate between core areas in different regional seas through marine straits, while specific coastal corridors (underwater) through river mouths and estuaries enable other species such as salmon *(Salmo salar)*, eels *(Anguilla anguilla)*, and sticklebacks *(Gasterosteus sp)* to migrate between river catchments and the sea.

Commuting corridors
• Commuting corridors facilitate the regular movements, mainly of vertebrates, from resting/breeding sites to foraging areas; otters *(Lutra lutra)*, badgers *(Meles meles)* and arctic foxes *(Alopex lagopus)* commute over distances of 10-50 km.

Dispersal corridors
• Dispersal corridors are used by individuals or populations to move from their sites of birth or former breeding areas to new breeding areas; salmon *(Salmo salar)* disperse over a distance of 100-1000 km.
• There is also dispersed marine migration (underwater) of cetaceans and various other species   between core areas in different parts of oceans.

Connecting corridors
• Bear *(Ursus arctos)*, lynx *(Lynx lynx)* and wolf *(Canis lupus)* are extending their ranges towards the core of the Alpine Range (the bear from the east, the lynx from the west and the wolf from the south and, possibly, from the east as well) using the entire Alpine arc as a connecting corridor.

Eurasian lynx

A high species immigration rate can contribute to maintaining species numbers, increasing meta-population size by preventing in-breeding and to increasing genetic variability. Furthermore, ecological corridors help to ensure ecosystem self-regulation capacity by enabling key species to move between ecosystem patches.

Individual corridors are not necessarily linear features, but can be grouped in several ways according to their shapes (diffuse, belt-like, line-like, etc.), structure (continuous or interrupted like stepping stones), relationship to core areas (conjunctive corridor or blind corridors), or by services provided such as migration corridors, commuting corridors and dispersal corridors (Foppen *et al.*, 2000), etc. Corridors do not necessarily have legal protection throughout their entire length, although certain sections or elements may be protected areas in their own right. However, to ensure that corridors retain their functionality, agreements concerning land and resource use are frequently necessary.

Buffer zones

Buffer zones are areas around the core areas and (around linking elements if necessary) that serve as protection from adverse external damage and disturbance. They aim to control human activities within the land adjacent to the core protected area by promoting their sound management, thus decreasing potential impacts and the probability of isolation. Buffer zones may perform a corridor function or harbour valuable biodiversity, such as species populations that are dependent on certain traditional forms of agriculture. Land-use management is a critical factor in the degree to which buffer zones can in practice prove to be effective as a conservation instrument. The current approach in buffer zone design tends to accept them as areas where a plan of land-use regulations is applied rather than as clearly defined areas that could have legal protection (Jongman, 2004).

Restoration areas

These are areas where measures are planned to develop the natural environment so that the areas' ecological functions can be restored.

Designing ecological networks

European ecological networks vary as to their function, spatial scale and the criteria that have been used for identification. The approach to applying the ecological network concept varies widely throughout Europe, and different methods and information sources have been used in the past to design ecological networks. They often depend on social, political, geographical or bio-geographical contexts. The design is often based on information regarding the occurrence of natural and landscape values in a country combined with expert judgement.

There are three main conceptual approaches to ecological networks, but in many cases a combination of the three approaches is used when a network is designed.

Eco-stabilising approach

This approach focuses on complexes of communities and species and aims at maintaining a coherent spatial structure of mutually interconnected ecosystems. It has been the basis for the Estonian, Lithuanian, and Russian networks. It is also the basis for the Territorial System of Ecological Stability (TSES) of the Landscape in the Czech Republic and in Slovakia. In these plans the relationship between human land use and the ecologically stabilising landscape functions has been emphasised. The eco-stabilising approach focuses on managing existing natural resources instead of restoring them or creating new ones. Based on the concepts of Rodoman (1974) the carrying capacity of the landscape and the division of land between anthropocentric core areas, buffer zones and ecotones on the one hand and large natural ecosystems on the other hand with transition zones in between is a key element.

Bio-ecological approach

This approach concentrates on targeted species and stresses recovery or restoration plans. In a landscape ecology perspective it is more process-oriented than the eco-stabilising approach. The bio-ecological approach is mainly used in Western Europe, particularly in the Netherlands and Belgium. Switzerland also uses this approach while taking into account the potential for landscape development.

In this approach, firstly the area or ecosystem that the ecological network will cover is assessed according to the presence of habitats for selected target species. Focus commonly is on keystone species (top predators, e.g. wolf, brown bear, otter), ecological engineers (e.g. beaver) and/or "umbrella" species (e.g. red deer) whose habitat requirements cover those of other species.

Information on the required quality and quantity of habitats for these groups of species is used to help identify the different potential populations and to determine whether they can be considered viable or sustainable. Then an ecological network is designed defining the core areas, ecological corridors, buffer zones and restoration areas (Jongman, 2004). The identification of corridors for species is complex. Accurate and validated information on species connectivity requirements is scarce, as are empirical data on the long-term functioning of existing ecological corridors. Especially when designing ecological networks on a larger geographical scale, i.e. national or international ecological networks, the selection of target species and the ensuing definition of corridors require careful consideration to ensure that as wide a range of species as possible will eventually benefit from the network. Corridors can be identified based on:
• information regarding the location of dispersal or migration routes of species;
• identification based on connectivity analysis of the landscape with various models;
• location of geomorphological features of the landscape, often river valleys (Biró *et al.*, 2006).

The beaver and its work

Greenways approach

Greenways are open natural or semi-natural areas that have a linear form and that have been planned in a multifunctional perspective: ecological, recreational and aesthetic. Most of them surround urban areas and provide opportunities for easy public access to 'nature' in a greener landscape. Although mostly developed on the American continent, this approach was incorporated after the 1970s in land-use planning in some regions in Europe, e.g. in the Lisbon area (Portugal). It is increasingly used in Europe at regional or local scale.

Stakeholder involvement in the design of ecological networks

Ecological networks in Europe are being developed mainly through national or regional governmental programmes and policies, sometimes initiated or stimulated by NGOs, such as WWF or IUCN, or through the framework of the Pan-European Biological and Landscape Diversity Strategy or other European-scale initiatives.

Ecological networks are usually designed at regional and national level, but they are actually implemented at local level. In certain respects, the implementation of ecological networks is more complex and challenging than more traditional approaches to the conservation of biodiversity and ecosystems. A large section of any ecological network will cover territory that is not designated or protected under any conservation law or regulation, and it stands to reason that these sections of the network will be in use for non-conservation purposes. Therefore, interaction and co-operation with the stakeholders involved in various forms of land use (agriculture, spatial planning, water management, infrastructure, housing, recreation, etc.) is a crucial part of the design and implementation of ecological networks. The older national ecological network programmes in Central Europe, for instance, were already based on an approach that would now be called sustainable development and were applied in detail at local level through the comprehensive planning systems in those countries. Most government-driven programmes also use the spatial-planning system – but also a range of other instruments such as financial incentives – to promote the sustainable use of biodiversity (Jongman, 2004).

The development of ecological networks is aimed primarily at conserving and restoring ecological connectivity through a system of core areas, buffer zones and biological interconnections. The main purpose of corridors is to maintain or re-establish links between different matrices of the ecological network. The development of ecological networks also has an impact at an ecological, cultural, aesthetic and even sociological level. As well as restoring links between areas of unspoilt land, the re-introduction of natural zones around urban areas has the effect of re-establishing links between people and nature, and between city-dwellers and rural areas. The restoration of ecological interconnections also benefits rural areas, particularly when in countering soil erosion and flooding.

Irish rural life

Developing an ecological network for a continent: the Pan-European Ecological Network

The policy framework of the Pan-European Ecological Network

PEEN is a key component of the Pan-European Biological and Landscape Diversity Strategy, endorsed in Sofia in 1995. This Strategy introduces a co-ordinating and unifying framework for strengthening and building upon existing initiatives. Furthermore, the Strategy seeks to integrate ecological considerations more effectively into all relevant socio-economic sectors, and will increase public participation in, and awareness and acceptance of, conservation interests.

The first Action Plan was the basis for the short-term implementation of the Strategy. It identified the actions to be undertaken between 1996 and 2000. At the end of this period, there was a review leading to the initiation of a new Action Plan for a further five-year period. This second Action Plan, renamed the Rolling Work Programme for the Strategy, was formally adopted in January 2003 (Annex 2).

One of the most important means through which the aim of the Strategy of integrating ecological considerations more effectively into all relevant socio-economic sectors will

Sensibilisation as from childhood

be achieved is the establishment of the Pan-European Ecological Network: *"The Pan-European Ecological Network will contribute to achieving the main goals of the Strategy by ensuring that a full range of ecosystems, habitats, species and their genetic diversity, and landscapes of European importance are conserved; habitats are large enough to place species in a favourable conservation status; there are sufficient opportunities for the dispersal and migration of species."*(Council of Europe *et al.*, 1996).

In order to achieve this, it is necessary to ensure the conservation of the characteristic ecosystems and the natural habitats and landscapes of European importance across their traditional ranges, the sustainable use of semi-natural habitats and cultural landscapes of European importance, the maintenance of

Hoopoe

viable populations of species of European importance across their traditional ranges and the maintenance of the environmental processes on which these ecosystems, habitats, species and landscapes depend.

The Pan-European Ecological Network promotes synergy between existing nature policies, land-use planning and rural and urban development. The PEEN concept offers a dynamic framework for integrating the policies of several sectors into the nature conservation and management approach; it will build upon and benefit from existing agreements, programmes and initiatives in the field of nature conservation. PEEN is also an overarching framework for ecological networks in Europe.

Adopted by the Council for the Pan-European Biological and Landscape Diversity Strategy on 21 April 1999, the

Guidelines for the development of the Pan-European Ecological Network are a reference document for use by all players involved in the development and implementation of the Pan-European Ecological Network, including policymakers, parliamentarians, natural resource managers, spatial planners, researchers, the academic community, representative organizations, private enterprises andmembersofnon-governmentalorganizations, on how to implement PEEN (Council of Europe, 1999).

The aim of establishing a Pan-European Ecological Network was reinforced in 2003 at the Fifth Environment for Europe Ministerial Conference in Kyiv which produced a PEEN Action Plan, followed by the Kyiv Resolution on Biodiversity. Its objectives include the identification and mapping of PEEN by 2006 in all States of the Pan-European region and appropriate conservation of all core areas of the Pan-European Ecological Network by 2008 (Annex 3).

The Pan-European Ecological Network's components

The Pan-European Ecological Network will be built up from three functionally complementary components: (a) core areas that provide the optimum achievable quantity and quality of environmental space, (b) corridors to ensure appropriate interconnectivity between the core areas, and (c) buffer zones to protect the core areas and corridors from potentially damaging external influences.

Ideally, the core areas will contain important representative examples from the characteristic European natural and semi-natural habitat types across their traditional range and at different stages of ecological succession, viable populations of species of European importance, the natural environmental processes on which these habitats and species populations depend and landscapes of European importance. Their conservation will be secured through: (a) full implementation of the existing international instruments that provide for the protection of important sites in Europe, particularly Natura 2000 under the EU Habitats Directive and the Emerald

Network under the Bern Convention, and (b) the policies and programmes of national and regional authorities.

Ecological corridors are intended to ensure that species populations have adequate opportunities for dispersal, migration and genetic exchange. The Committee of Experts for the Development of PEEN has adopted the following typology: Corridors are defined in a broad sense as links between habitat resources of a species consisting of a landscape structure that is different from the matrix surrounding it thus favouring the propagation of the species (individuals, seeds, genes).

This definition is based on the functionality of the corridor and implies that linear-shaped habitat without the purpose of linking two areas at both ends cannot be defined as a corridor.

The buffer zones are intended to protect the core areas and corridors of the Pan-European Ecological Network from the effects of potentially damaging external influences. Buffer zones will often offer reasonably wide scope for other land uses and may offer important conservation benefits in themselves.

Restoration of habitats will be a priority where habitat fragmentation has seriously disrupted the functioning of ecosystems or has substantially reduced the opportunities for species populations of European importance to survive. It will also be important in areas that have a high potential biological diversity value but which have been physically disrupted or polluted.

It may be appropriate as part of a restoration project to consider the reintroduction of species where this would benefit the functioning of the particular ecosystem or would restore the indigenous species communities. However, re-introductions should only be undertaken where certain conditions are met (Council of Europe, 1999).

Marine and coastal ecological networks

The issues of coastal and marine ecological networks have received special attention in the framework of the Pan-European Ecological Network and PEBLDS. The Executive Bureau of PEBLDS designated EUCC-The Coastal Union together with the Council of Europe and UNEP as the responsible body for the establishment of the European Coastal and Marine Ecological

European bee-eaters

Network (ECMEN). Two reports on ECMEN and a map of the coastal systems of Europe have since been prepared and published.

In the context of PEEN the European Coastal and Marine Ecological Network has five main aims:
1. to raise awareness of the importance of a network approach to the conservation of habitats and species at pan-European level, and thereby encourage the development of networks;
2. to provide a platform facilitating co-ordination and co-operation between existing and proposed networks at local, national, and regional scales;
3. to identify gaps in the current approaches to site and species conservation;
4. to supply the scientific data necessary for network development, adding value by situating individual initiatives in a Pan-European context;
5. to provide support for local and national initiatives in network-building.

The implementation of the Pan-European Ecological Network

Designing and implementing an ecological network – especially if a larger territory is to be covered or if the network crosses national or administrative borders – generally combines top-down and bottom-up approaches. This is reflected in the PEEN implementation process. In fact, since practical implementation of ecological networks can only take place on a fairly limited geographical scale, PEEN will have to be based on national and regional ecological networks, with cross-boundary collaboration being the main element for cohesion and coherence across the continent (bottom-up approach). This approach sees PEEN mostly as a framework concept that stimulates initiatives at all levels and creates synergy with a view to mitigating the effects of fragmentation.

However, it is unlikely that PEEN will develop automatically if and when all countries of Europe have developed national ecological networks. Experience shows that the development of national and regional ecological networks does not always occur in an international perspective, even when the network is being developed in a border region. Therefore, establishing a Pan-European Ecological Network requires a certain amount of top-down guidance; elements of PEEN could for example be identified according to pan-European criteria (Rientjes & Roumelioti, 2003). This approach requires considerable collaboration between countries in implementing the different elements of the network. PEEN could provide the framework for such co-operation.

So far many countries have already planned the development of national ecological networks. Map 3, which was presented at the Conference on Biodiversity in Europe in February 2006, provides an overview of a number of ecological networks that have been designed on a national or sub-national scale (Flanders) in the Pan-European region (the map includes only a part of the Draft Scheme of the Ecological Network of the Russian Federation presented by the Biodiversity Conservation Center in 2006 – see map 4). This map reveals, even if only partially, the variety of approaches adopted across Europe. The map and questionnaire that were distributed by the Council of Europe to the national PEEN experts at the end of 2004 show that national ecological networks in Europe vary greatly in:
• geographical scale (designed for a whole country or designed for regions as in Belgium, Germany or, in certain

respects, Russia);
• types of core areas included (only nationally protected areas or nationally and internationally recognised sites as well, especially Natura 2000 sites in EU countries, Ramsar sites, etc.);and
• proportion of defined core areas and ecological corridors (like Ukraine or Hungary).

Tawny owl

Pygmy owls

Tengmalm's owls

It also emerged from the questionnaires that most of the European countries followed in one way or another the guidance of the Council of Europe on the identification of the elements of PEEN for the designation of their network at a national level. The purpose of the network was proved to be the same in most of the cases: ensuring ecological connectivity.

Some countries, however, regard their Natura 2000 networks as their national ecological networks (Sweden); others are not planning to identify a network, such as Norway on account of its wealth of natural areas, low population density, and low percentage of developed land areas (agriculture, industry, urban areas etc.).

Map 3 : Map of selected designed national and sub-national ecological networks in Europe (Source: ECNC [Tardy-Vegh-Zentai], 2006).

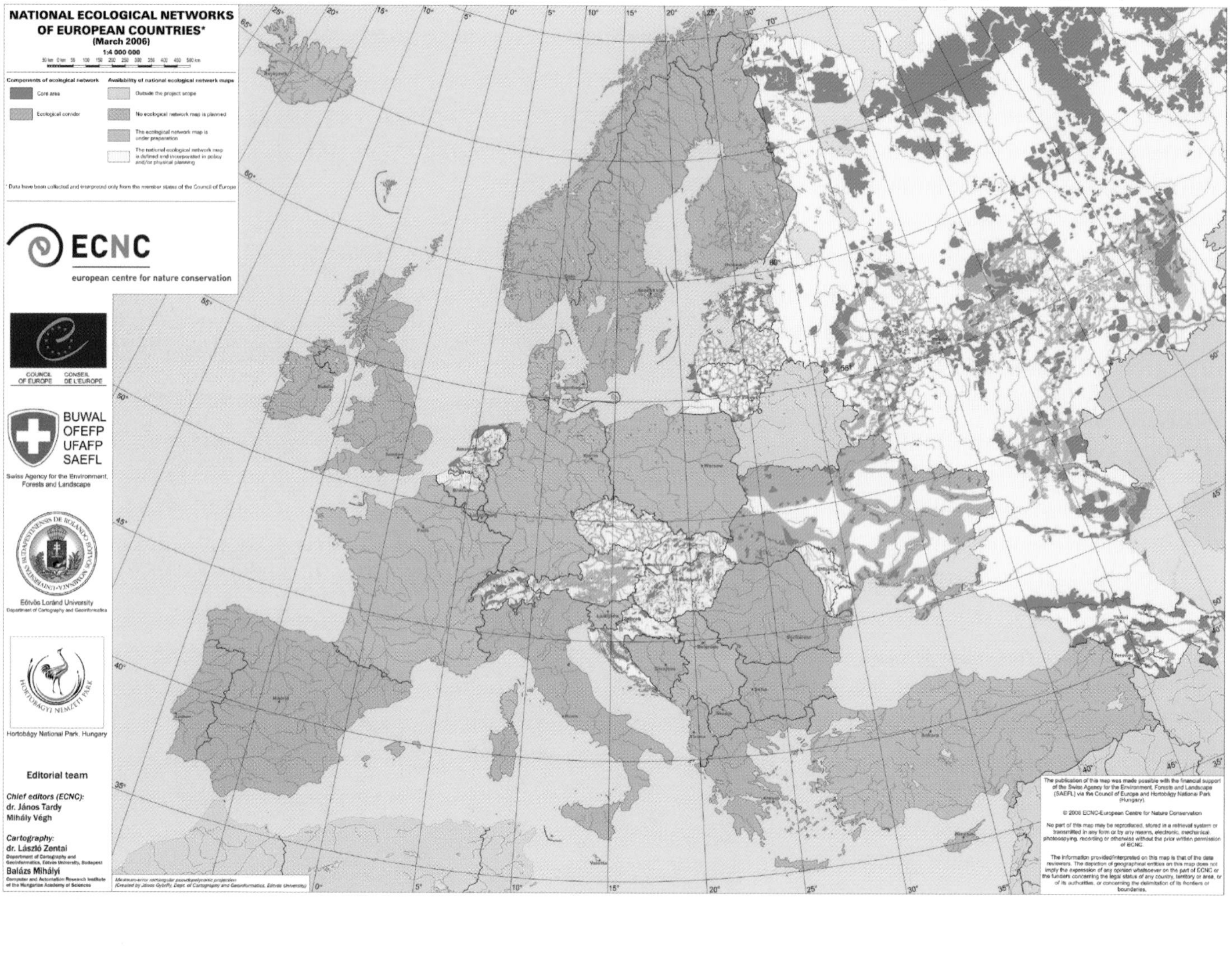

An indicative map covering the whole territory of the Federation of Russia has been prepared with the cooperation of several Russian authorities and organisations. This map presents the state of preparation of the general indicative cartography of the Russian Ecological Network (RUSECONET) at the end of 2006.

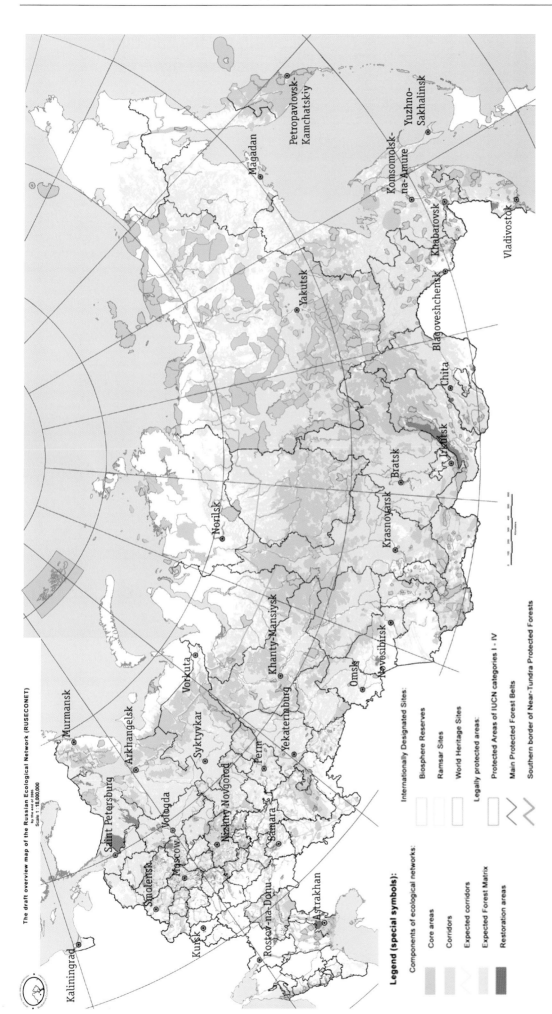

The draft overview map of the Russian Ecological Network (RUSECONET)
by the end of 2006
Scale 1 : 18,000,000

Legend (special symbols):

Components of ecological networks:

Core areas
Corridors
Expected corridors
Expected Forest Matrix
Restoration areas

Internationally Designated Sites:

Biosphere Reserves
Ramsar Sites
World Heritage Sites

Legally protected areas:

Protected Areas of IUCN categories I - IV
Main Protected Forest Belts
Southern border of Near-Tundra Protected Forests

Map 4 : General indicative map of the Russian ecological network (RUSECONET) at the end of 2006. (Source: Biodiversity Conservation Center (BCC), 2006). Special symbols used on the map: Components of ecological networks: core areas – Areas of ecological linkages: corridors; expected corridors; expected forest matrix –Restoration areas: Internationally designated sites: biosphere reserves; Ramsar sites ; world heritage sites – Legally protected areas: protected areas of IUCN categories I – IV; main protected forest belts; southern border of Near-Tundra protected forests.

Therefore, as can be seen here as well as will be shown in Chapter 3, both bottom-up and top-down approaches are being implemented in practice. While an increasing number of countries, regions and local communities are integrating ecological networks into their spatial planning, including through trans-boundary co-operation, international and European instruments providing the framework for the steady development of the elements of a 'physical' Pan-European Ecological Network.

Mapping the Pan-European Ecological Network

Mapping of the indicative locations of the core areas, ecological corridors and buffer zones of the Pan-European Ecological Network started in 2000. Based on an analysis of land cover, distribution of designated and recognised areas and the distribution of selected habitats and species that are considered especially relevant for the region and for the Pan-European Ecological Network in its entirety, the main component elements of the PEEN have been tentatively identified:

Map 5 : Indicative map of the Pan-European Ecological Network for Central and Eastern Europe (ECNC, 2002)..

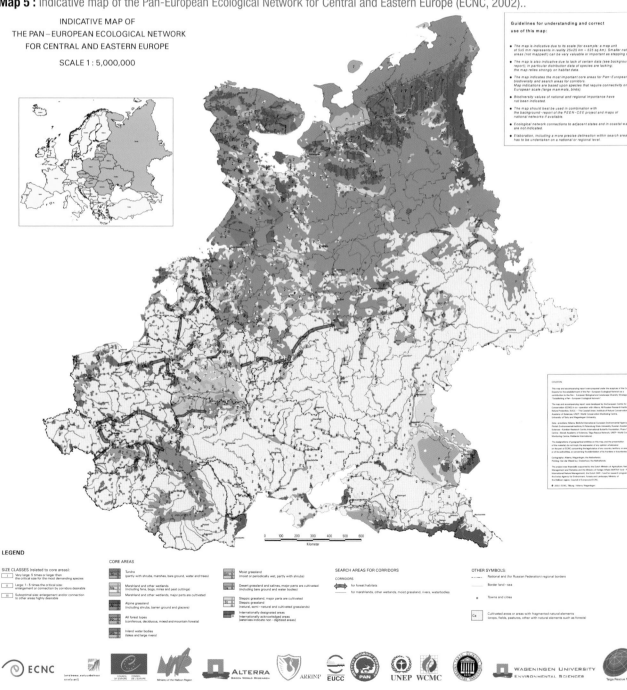

• core nature areas of European importance;
• existing corridors and stepping-stones between these areas;
• sites where new corridors could and should be established to meet the connectivity requirements of selected key species;
• the location of buffer zones, when and if required.

So far, the PEEN indicative map has been completed for Central and Eastern Europe: (2003 : Belarus, Czech Republic, Estonia, Hungaria, Latvia, Lithuania, Moldova, Poland, Romania, Federation of Russia, Slovak Republic, Ukraine [Bouwma *et al*, 2002]) and Southern and Eastern

Europe (Albania, Bosnia-Herzegovina, Bulgaria, Croatia, Cyprus, "The former Yugoslav Republic of Macedonia", Greece, Montenegro, Serbia, Slovenia, Turkey [Biro *et al*, 2006]). A similar process for Western Europe has been completed in 2006 (Source : Alterra, 2006). The indicative map for Switzerland has existed since 2004.

Chapter 3 shows various examples of regional approaches of PEEN, constituting frameworks for co-operation between neighbouring countries and regions.

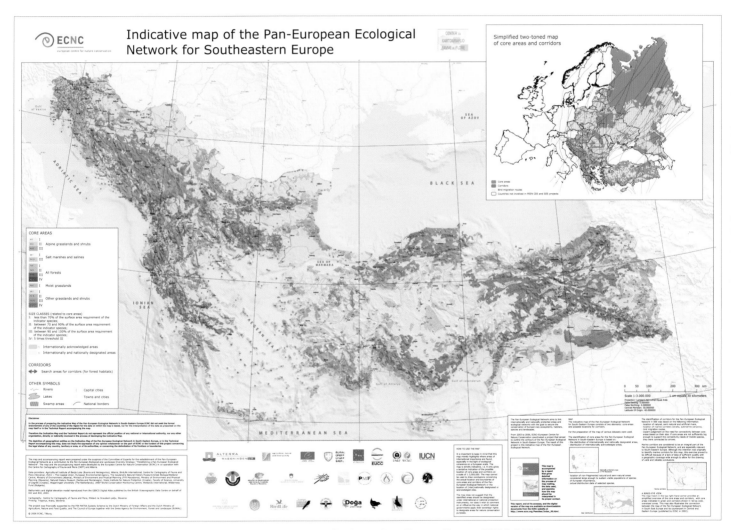

Map 6 : Indicative map of the Pan-European Ecological Network for South-East Europe (Source: ECNC, 2006).

Map 7 : Draft map of the Pan-European Ecological Network for Western Europe. This card may be subject to be revised in order to include new elements sent by the states (Source: Alterra, 2006)

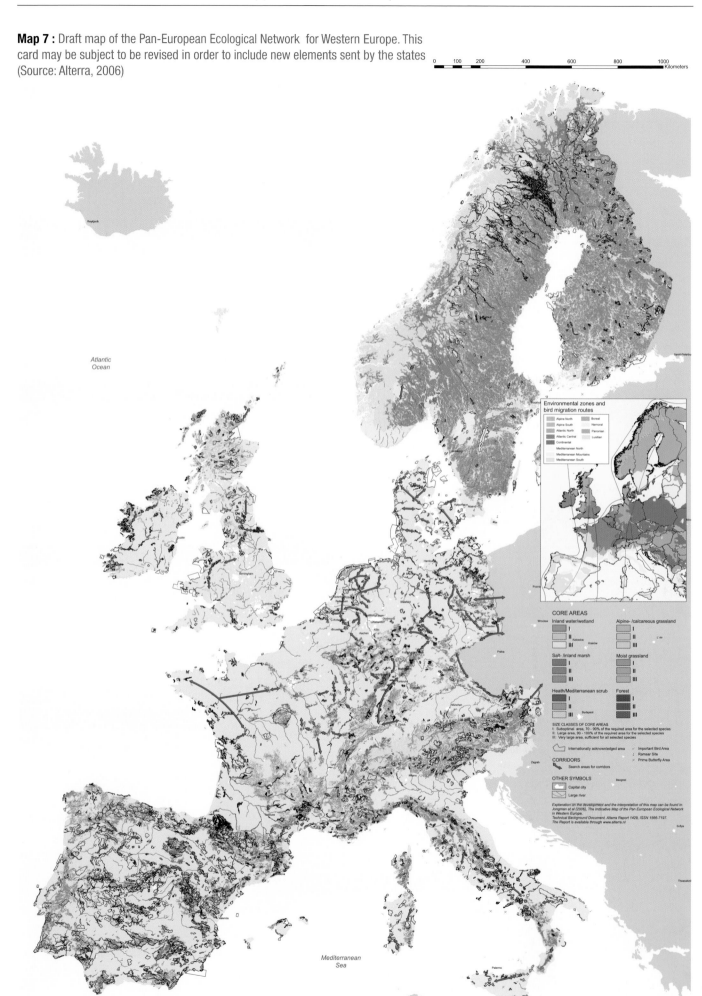

Conclusion

Based on scientific foundations, the ecological networks concept is developing as a framework that facilitates synergy between protection of biodiversity and sustainable social and economic development. It applies at different geographical scales, i.e. local, regional, national and international

Approaches by countries or regions in designing ecological networks differ depending on their historical tradition in land planning as well as on their biogeographical context. Although the relevance of ecological networks is increasingly acknowledged for the protection of habitats and species, it is also recognized that connectivity requirements vary greatly from species to species: what functions adequately as a corridor for one species may be relatively useless for another. Practical relevance and viability is therefore considered highest if a network focuses on specific species or habitats (ECNC, 2003, Rientjes & Roumelioti, 2003).

According to recommendations contained in the Pan-European Biological Diversity Strategy, the application of ecological network concepts must also be considered at Pan-European scale. Through the political endorsement of the Pan-European Ecological Network, emphasis is placed in particular on connectivity, comparably to the major international conservation legal and policy instruments.

Indicative maps of PEEN in various regions of Europe are being developed, highlighting potential needs for transboundary approaches in developing or maintaining corridors for selected species.

The following chapter will assess how various international and national systems of law and policy contribute to the establishment of PEEN and its component parts of core areas, corridors and buffer zones. In Chapter 3, an assessment will be made concerning the extent to which these component parts are currently operational.

Capercaillie : female

Capercaillie : male

CHAPTER

II

The legal background to ecological networks
in general and the Pan-European Ecological Network
in particular

European wolves (F)

V. Munier

Various international and Community legal instruments ...

are used to implement the Pan-European Biological and Landscape Diversity Strategy (PEBLDS) and serve, in turn, as foundations on which the Pan-European Ecological Network (PEEN) can be built. Only those which are mandatory will be considered in this chapter. In addition, several countries have introduced binding legislation for the establishment of ecological networks at national level and these will be discussed later in the chapter.

The international and European legal framework of the Pan-European Ecological Network

The legal basis for the Pan-European Ecological Network can be broadly divided into two conceptual categories. The first category includes requirements that arise from major international agreements on nature conservation and the second includes those that aim for sustainable spatial development. Here we take each of these types of legislation in turn.

International conventions on nature conservation

Many international conventions are relevant to the establishment of PEEN, primarily because they embrace provisions concerned with ecological connectivity between sites (Bonnin, 2004). As such, implementing ecological networks provides States with both a fresh approach to conserving biological diversity and a means of honouring their international obligations.

Several of the international conventions call on the Contracting Parties to designate protected areas, which constitute many of the core areas for PEEN. Some conventions also require the designation of buffer zones and contain provisions that can be used to set up biological corridors. In addition, most conventions advocate connectivity, either in the text itself or in the documents adopted by the Conferences of Parties. For greater clarity, these conventions are presented according to geographic focus.

Global conventions
Convention on Biological Diversity

The implementation of the PEEN within the context of PEBLDS represents a regional application of the aims of the Convention on Biological Diversity (CBD), and provides an important way of implementing the Ecosystem Approach, which was endorsed by the CBD at CoP5 in Kenya in 2000 as the primary framework for action under the Convention.

The CBD has three main goals: the conservation of biodiversity, its sustainable use, and the equitable sharing of costs and benefits. Although the convention text itself does not mention ecological networks, many of its provisions address the components of ecological connectivity. Article 8 (a) of the

Crane

CBD stipulates that *"each Contracting Party shall, as far as possible and as appropriate, establish a system of protected areas or areas where special measures need to be taken to conserve biological diversity."*

The use of the word 'system' facilitates an extensive interpretation of the text of the Convention. In fact, the guide to the Convention on Biological Diversity draws on Article 8 (a) to advocate *"the creation of a larger series of protected areas than would otherwise be necessary, associated with ecological corridors and staging areas between protected zones so that the species can move on as required by climate change."*

Furthermore, paragraphs (d) and (e) of Article 8 of the Convention emphasize the need to preserve nature outside protected areas and the importance of buffer areas by calling on the parties to *"promote environmentally sound and sustainable development in areas adjacent to protected areas with a view to furthering protection of these areas."*

The reference in paragraph (d) to 'viable populations' shows that what is at issue here is not just protected areas but all types of public and private areas. In most cases, preserving viable populations implies the movement of individuals between populations and sub-populations (as described by metapopulation theory; see Chapter 1), and thus requires protecting sufficiently large areas to enable populations to be maintained in a favourable conservation status and allow movement between the different habitats. Therefore to maintain an effective 'system of protected areas' countries will have to include connectivity between sites.

The Programme of Work (POW) on Protected Areas adopted at CoP7 was designed to ensure the establishment and preservation by 2010 for terrestrial areas and by 2012 for marine areas, of complete national and regional systems of protected areas (CBD, 2005). These networks should be sufficiently managed and ecologically representative, working together towards the aims of the Convention and the 2010 Commitment to significantly reduce the rate of biodiversity loss. Importantly for PEEN, the Programme calls for all protected areas to be integrated

Swallowtail

into their wider land- and seascapes by 2015. The implementation of the ecosystem approach broadly promoted by the CBD calls for the integration of protected areas with the relevant land use sectors. The CBD is the primary global agreement for nature conservation and therefore it is important for Parties to meet their commitments to it. While the Convention works towards global goals for the conservation and sustainable use of biodiversity, PEEN provides a useful tool with which to implement many of the objectives laid out in the POW on Protected Areas. COP8 has recalled the necessity of promoting the conservation of genetic diversity and, of special importance to PEEN, it recommends that the Parties make environmental impact assessments mandatory for 'activities in ecological corridors identified as being important for ecological or evolutionary processes'.

Ramsar Convention on Wetlands

The Convention on Wetlands of International Importance, which was signed in Ramsar in 1971, provides a framework for national action and international co-operation to ensure the conservation and wise use of wetlands and their resources. The new guidelines on the management of Ramsar sites adopted by its COP8 in 2002 recommend a zoning system to take account of the importance of connectivity among the core areas of the Ramsar sites. Furthermore the COP also urged Parties to take joint measures to ensure the management of transboundary wetlands. Section 16 of the second Strategic Action Plan for 2003-2008 pinpoints three main lines of action. Parties must endeavour to cooperate 'internationally

*Rapadalen Delta,
Lapland (S)*

in their delivery of wetland conservation and wise use, through the management of transboundary water resources and wetlands'. General Objective 2 goes even further in stipulating that the registration of transboundary sites should also be given priority.

By considering the wetland ecosystem in its entirety, the Ramsar Convention has been a pioneer in promoting the ecosystem approach. This Convention also calls on Parties to protect areas which can represent core areas of PEEN. Another important feature is that the Convention pays special attention to the conservation of migratory bird populations, which raises issues concerning connectivity between core areas.

World Heritage Convention

The World Heritage Convention was the first convention to make it possible to protect nature on a global scale. Its main objective is to identify and preserve the world's cultural and natural heritage and sites are designated to be protected for the 'common heritage of humankind'. The Convention does not aim to protect the sites themselves but to ensure that national governments do so. However, the importance of conservation is greatly increased by the fact that States recognize that such heritage 'constitutes a world heritage for whose protection it is the duty of the international community as a whole to cooperate' (Article 6). The fact that this duty to co-operate is set out in a legally binding convention may be particularly useful when setting up an ecological network, especially in transboundary areas. The Convention is also important because of it makes it possible to protect landscapes and raise awareness about them in their cultural as well as their natural aspects. It has the ability to protect core areas, buffer zones and corridors

Bonn Convention

The restoration or protection of migration routes is one of the functions inherent in the ecological network concept. The Convention on the Conservation of Migratory Species of Wild Animals, which was signed in Bonn in 1979, introduced a specific convention system for migratory species, making it one of the fundamental points of departure for

Great crested grebe (CH)

PEEN. What makes this Convention unique is that it aims at protecting migration as a process far beyond protection of species and areas.

The agreements negotiated in connection with this convention are also particularly

Otter

important. For example, the African-Eurasian Waterbird Agreement of 1995 relates to bird species' entire ranges in an effort to ensure that there are no breaks in the protection afforded along migration routes. This agreement does not just create protected areas but calls on the parties to regulate human activities which may affect the conservation status of the migratory species concerned. Since the restoration or protection of migration routes is one of the keys to the creation of ecological corridors, this agreement contributes to the establishment of such corridors, as advocated by PEEN.

European conventions

Several international conventions for which the geographical scope is the European continent are relevant to the implementation of PEEN. Applied at regional scale, these legal texts are particularly adapted to the European situation as regards nature protection. They are particularly important for PEEN, in terms of protection of both species and areas.

Bern Convention

The Bern Convention on the Conservation of European Wildlife and Natural Habitats of 1979 was drawn up with a view to increasing inter-State co-operation on nature conservation. Article 4 of the Convention stresses the importance of transboundary protected areas. The Standing Committee of this Convention has repeatedly invited States to introduce ecological networks. In 1991, for instance, it adopted Recommendation No. 25 on the conservation of natural areas outside protected areas proper, advising Contracting

Parties to 'encourage the conservation and, where necessary, the restoration of ecological corridors'. The Recommendation goes on to list various types of corridor, such as rights of way of roads, railways and watercourses. This text is certainly the most important one adopted by the Standing Committee of the Bern Convention in the field of biological interconnections. However, there are other Recommendations inviting States to establish ecological networks for specific species, such as Recommendation No. 53 of 1996 on the conservation of the European otter *(Lutra lutra)*. Standing Committee Recommendations in 1989 and 1996 were also the basis on which the Emerald Network was set up. The Committee recommends that, in order to preserve this network of natural habitats, the Parties 'take steps to designate Areas of Special Conservation Interest' (the practical aspects are described in section 3 below). These areas are in many cases included as core areas for PEEN.

European Landscape Convention

By inviting States to promote the protection, management and development of European landscapes and supporting co-operation in this field this Convention, which was signed in Florence in October 2000, has reinforced the legal basis for creating PEEN. Article 9 of the Convention relates to transboundary landscapes and states that: *"Parties shall encourage transboundary co-operation on local and regional levels and, wherever necessary, prepare and implement joint landscape programmes."*

Falsterbo, Scania (S)

This Article is particularly interesting in that it could prove useful for the establishment of transboundary corridors not necessarily involving the creation of a new transboundary protected area. The political fragmentation of these areas is sometimes reflected in the existence of fences or the practice of clear-felling along borders. Co-operation to conserve these transboundary habitats would seem therefore to be a means of setting up international corridors. Furthermore, Article 5(d) of the Convention calls on the Parties to integrate landscapes into town and spatial planning policies. Linear landscape features provide biological interconnections which it is important to preserve as corridors within PEEN.

Convention on the protection of the Alps

The Alpine Convention, which is a framework convention designed to guarantee the protection and sustainable development of the Alps, has been the subject of several implementing protocols which now serve as points of departure for the establishment of PEEN (see the description of the Alpine Network in Section 3 below). For example, the Protocol on the Implementation of the Convention in the field of Nature Protection and Landscape Conservation, signed in December 1994, includes several provisions on the conservation of natural habitats. Article 12 of the Protocol is entitled 'The Ecological Network' and requires Parties to take appropriate action to set up a national and transboundary network of existing protected areas, biotopes and other objects, whether protected or requiring protection.

The Multi-Annual Work Programme of the Alpine Convention has included among its priorities measures to network transboundary protected areas and link up with other structures of ecological importance over the next six years. This protocol also calls on parties to harmonise aims and measures applicable to transboundary protected areas. By encouraging the creation of transboundary protected areas, the Alpine conventional system promotes the maintenance of large natural complexes that can contribute to PEEN as core areas, buffer zones and corridors, in particular for large carnivores.

Tatras mountains (SK/PL)

Carpathian Convention

The Framework Convention for the protection and sustainable development of the Carpathian mountains, signed in Kiev in 2003, recognizes the exceptional ecological value of the Carpathian region and provides the legal background for the sustainable

Mouflon, ibex chamois

protection of its ecosystems. Parties are requested to take appropriate measures to ensure a high level of protection of natural and semi-natural habitats, as well as their continuity and connectivity. This Convention is the first international agreement to refer explicitly to the need for Parties to implement a Carpathian ecological network, as an integral part of PEEN. Furthermore the Convention calls for the integrated management of river basins in order to reduce fragmentation of aquatic habitats. In addition the Convention recognizes the importance of biodiversity integration in sectoral policies.

Networks of protected areas in regional seas

The marine Conventions described below contribute to the establishment of PEEN by setting up regional networks of protected areas that centre on a specific ecosystem: the regional sea. These conventions help to protect both the seas themselves and coastal areas, which are particularly vulnerable to fragmentation as a result of urbanization. These networks cross borders and allow regional issues in the protected areas to be viewed in terms of ecosystems.

❸

Integrated coastal area management as recommended by the Council of Europe

The Model law on the sustainable management of coastal areas and the code of conduct for coastal areas. drawn up by the Council of Europe, contains precise and concrete recommendations that can help facilitate the sustainable development of coastal areas (Council of Europe, 2004 and 2003/2).

The new Protocol concerning Mediterranean Specially Protected Areas (Barcelona Convention, 1995), adopted to implement the Convention for the Protection of the Marine Environment and the Coastal Region of the Mediterranean, aims to set up a network of specially protected areas intended to preserve endangered natural habitats or habitats essential to the survival of endangered species. The launch in 2005, by the Regional Activity Centre for Specially Protected Areas,

of a Mediterranean action plan for the conservation of the bird species listed in Appendix 2 contributes to PEEN by focusing on sites of special ecological interest. The main aim of this plan is to preserve and/or restore the population levels of these bird species.

The system of protected coastal and marine areas in the Baltic set up in 1994 under the Helsinki Convention on the Protection of the Maritime Environment of the Baltic Sea Area of 1992 also establishes core areas for PEEN. A joint project, run by the Baltic Marine Environment Protection Commission (the Helsinki Commission – HELCOM) and the Commission for the Protection of the Marine Environment of the North-East Atlantic (OSPAR), is of particular relevance to PEEN. This project is based on a shared work programme for the creation of a joint network of protected marine areas by 2010. The idea of setting up joint OSPAR/HELCOM marine conservation areas is in keeping with the aims of the PEEN, one of which is to promote synergy between partners working for the protection of natural sites.

The 1992 Convention on the Protection of the Black Sea against Pollution has given rise to many schemes for the protection of natural habitats. They include the Black Sea Environmental Programme, which organizes conservation work in habitats that are critical for populations of priority species. The forthcoming application of the recent Black Sea Biodiversity and Landscapes Conservation Protocol, signed in Bulgaria in 2003, will also make it easier to identify and protect important natural habitats in the Black Sea region and thus to establish core areas there for PEEN.

Highlands cattle (Wadden Sea, NL)

Razorbill (ICL)

4 Developing ecological MPA networks in the Mediterranean

Sardinian coast (I)

S. Hellio

In accordance with the resolution endorsed by States during the World Summit on Sustainable Development (Johannesburg, 2002) to establish representative networks of marine protected areas (MPAs) by 2012, the need arises to establish a system of MPAs that is truly representative of the full Mediterranean habitats. Several initiatives already exist to address conservation concerns at the regional level for the identification of Mediterranean MPAs and the setting up of marine ecological networks in the Mediterranean area.

In the framework of the Barcelona Convention, specially protected areas of Mediterranean importance have been established (SPAMIs). The EU Natura 2000 network, the Emerald Network of the Bern Convention (Council of Europe), the UNESCO Biosphere Reserves and the World Heritage Sites represent important instruments for the designation of Mediterranean marine protected sites. The World Commission on Protected Areas (WCPA) of IUCN has initiated a programme of support the Barcelona framework in catalysing regional, national and local efforts to design and establish MPAs, and in improving protected area legislation to allow the WSSD target to be met. A Network of Managers of Marine Protected Areas in the Mediterranean (MedPAN) has also been launched by WWF in 2005 and brings together representatives of 11 countries (8 European countries and 3 North-African countries).

Other international instruments relevant to the concept of ecological networks

Some international agreements are not directly related to nature conservation but are nevertheless important for the establishment of PEEN as they contribute to the implementation of the principles and aims of PEEN and the governing Strategy (PEBLDS). For instance the convention system which sets

5 PEEN and public participation

For PEEN to be applied in the field, the public has to be involved, and the Convention on Access to Information, Public Participation in Decision-making and Access to Justice in Environmental Matters, signed in Aarhus in 1998, will therefore serve as a supporting instrument.

up mechanisms for international co-operation, such as the two Benelux Conventions on the protection of birds and hunting and the nature conservation and landscape protection respectively, and European bodies such as the Congress of Local and Regional Authorities of the Council of Europe and the European Commission's Committee of the

Regions contribute to an approach based on connectivity. Similarly, the Aarhus Convention, which requires that the public be involved in decisions on the environment, also constitutes a way of achieving the objectives of PEEN through stakeholder involvement. Integrating environmental concerns into sectoral policies is also crucial to PEEN, as emphasized in various international instruments such as the Guiding Principles for Sustainable Spatial Development and the Convention system for the protection of air quality.

International corridors and transboundary co-operation between local authorities

Transboundary co-operation between local and regional authorities can make a vital contribution to the creation of transboundary biological corridors because it fosters concerted action on land use and nature conservation. Changes to legislation on transboundary co-operation have led to the emergence of a stable and appropriate legal framework and the implementation of initiatives enhancing the connectivity of natural habitats.

In the first European Outline Convention on Transboundary Co-operation between Territorial Communities or Authorities

(Madrid 1980), States undertook to 'facilitate and foster transboundary co-operation'. The agreements provided under this convention cover various fields, including regional development and environmental protection. Its operative provisions are somewhat brief but they are completed by a series of appendices in the form of 'outline agreements, statutes and contracts', which serve as models of documents that national governments can sign to arrange transboundary co-operation between local authorities under various hypothetical circumstances. These model

6

PEEN and air quality

By encouraging the rational management, conservation and, where necessary, the expansion of greenhouse gas sinks and reservoirs not governed by the Montreal Protocol, including biomass, forests and oceans and other land, coastal and marine ecosystems, the 1992 Convention on Climate Change provides an opportunity to integrate the preservation of ecological infrastructures favourable to biodiversity

international agreements are intended to establish the framework, the procedures and the limits within which states wish local and regional authorities to act. The aim of the Additional Protocol of 1995 was to strengthen the Outline Convention by expressly granting local and regional authorities the right to negotiate transboundary co-operation agreements under certain circumstances.

Changes in international and national law on transboundary co-operation have made it possible to set up various types of bodies and systems and move closer to the goal of transboundary natural heritage management.

Guiding Principles for Sustainable Spatial Development

At the 12th session of the European Conference of Ministers responsible for Regional Planning (CEMAT), in Hanover in 2000, the ministers adopted the Guiding Principles for Sustainable Spatial Development of the European Continent. These Principles make a number of references to ecological networks. They state, among other things, that spatial planning policy *'is concerned with re-establishing and conserving ecosystems including ecological networks'*. The Principles are not binding but they were the subject of a recommendation by the Committee of Ministers on 30 January 2002, which gives them political weight.

European Community instruments

The European Union has adopted strong legislation on the protection of animal and plant species and their habitats, and is increasingly addressing the problem of fragmented natural habitats. Many other Community policies and legal texts which do not address nature protection directly can help to establish the PEEN, including documents on agriculture, transport and water management.

Isola 2000 (F)

7

Direct legal references to ecological coherence in the Habitats Directive

Preamble
In order to ensure the restoration or maintenance of natural habitats and species (...) at a favourable conservation status, it is necessary to (...) create a coherent European ecological network.
Article 1
Site of community importance means a site which (...) may also contribute significantly to the coherence of

Natura 2000 referred to in Article 3, and/or contributes significantly to the maintenance of biological diversity within the biogeographic region or regions concerned.
Article 3
3. (...) Member states shall endeavour to improve the ecological coherence of Natura 2000 by maintaining, and where appropriate developing, features of the landscape which are of major importance for wild fauna and flora, as referred to in Article 10.

Article 4
(...) the member state concerned shall designate that site as a special area of conservation (...) establishing priorities (...) for the coherence of Natura 2000.
Article 10
Member states shall endeavour, where they consider it necessary, in their land-use planning and development policies and, in particular, with a view to improving the ecological coherence of the Natura 2000 network, to encourage the management of features of the landscape which are of major importance for wild fauna and flora.

Community instruments for conservation of biodiversity

The Birds and Habitats Directives which lay down the legal basis for the Natura 2000 network are the most influential nature conservation instruments at European Community level. However, the connectivity approach in Community law on nature conservation is shown more clearly in the development of the Biodiversity Strategy and associated action plans, as well as in the EC Communication on Biodiversity.

The Natura 2000 network

The Natura 2000 network is one of the most important networks of sites for the establishment of PEEN. Based on stable legal regulations, the network requires EU member states to propose, and then designate, sites under two directives: Directive 79/409/EEC (1979) on the conservation of wild birds and Directive 92/43/EEC (1992) on the conservation of natural habitats and of wild fauna and flora, the aim being to preserve species and habitats regarded as being of

Fishing in a pond of Brenne (F)

Community interest. Comprising Special Protection Areas under the Birds Directive, and Special Areas of Conservation under the Habitats Directive, the Natura 2000 network makes an essential contribution to identification and designation of the core areas in PEEN.

The Special Protection Areas designated under the Birds Directive have to be protected by national legislation by the date of submission to the European Commission. For sites designated under the Habitats Directive the procedure required is slightly different. After the lists of sites have

been adopted for biogeographical regions Member States must establish the necessary conservation measures. Although the network's purpose – *"to ensure a favourable conservation status of the ecosystems, habitats, species and landscapes of European importance "*
– is defined at European level, it is up to each country to decide how to achieve it. Depending on a national legislative framework and conservation objectives of sites, preference will thus go to strict protection or integrated management planning. Some sites raise socio-economic issues, and finding the best way of reconciling these various concerns is also one of the network's aims.

Setting up the network involves a lengthy process of consultation, which has been under way since 1995, between the national authorities responsible for protecting biodiversity in each country, the European Commission and the European Environment Agency, which has the task of analysing and comparing approaches to proposing and designating sites at European level. Scientists, NGOs and representatives of nature users (farmers, foresters, hunters, anglers, etc.) are also involved, inter alia through the process called Seminars for Biogeographical Regions.

The Natura 2000 network promotes more consistent classification of areas by different countries within the different European biogeographical regions. The key concept of 'favourable conservation status', which is the basis of the Habitats Directive, suggests that the conservation of species and habitats recognized as being of Community interest must take account of species' capacities for migration, dispersal and reproduction, along with the functional character of habitats.

Article 10 of the Habitats Directive refers to the concept of corridors, although it does not strictly recognise corridors as such or render them mandatory. The Article reads as follows: *"Member States shall endeavour, where they consider it necessary, in their land-use planning and development policies and, in particular, with a view to improving the ecological coherence of the Natura 2000 network, to encourage the management of features of the landscape which are of major importance for wild fauna and flora'.*

Such features are those which, by virtue of their linear and continuous structure (such as rivers with their banks, or traditional systems for marking field boundaries) or their function as stepping-stones (such as ponds or small woods), are essential for the migration, dispersal and genetic exchange of wild species."

Despite the limited binding force of this Article, it is important to stress that the aim of maintaining biological connections was very much to the fore in the preparation of the Directive, and the precise identification of elements whose protection the States might encourage shows that the Natura 2000 network is now increasingly taking ecological fragmentation into account.

Whiskerd terns

be created between Natura 2000 sites within and between EU countries.

As a follow-up to an extensive review of the EC Biodiversity Strategy and Action Plans, the Malahide Message supported by the European Council's conclusions (June 2004) set out priorities and goals to meet the 2010 commitment to halt the loss of biodiversity in the EU.

This Message has been further endorsed and considerably enhanced within an integrated approach by the Communication from the Commission 'Halting the loss of biodiversity by 2010 and beyond - Sustaining ecosystem services for human well-being' published in May 2006. The Communication on Biodiversity Objective 1 of the Communication on Biodiversity calls on Member States to reinforce the coherence and connectivity of the Natura 2000 network. It also highlights the need to restore biodiversity and ecosystem services in non-protected rural areas of the EU. Compliance with these objectives by Member States is crucial to the implementation of PEEN within the EU.

Environmental Action Plans, EC Biodiversity Strategy and EC Biodiversity Communication

The ecological network concept was first incorporated into Community environmental policy with the 5th Community Action Programme for the Environment, which advocated creating an 'inter-related network of habitats, based on the concept for Natura 2000'. The 6th Environment Action Programme 2002-2012 refers to the Community Strategy on Biological Diversity adopted in 1998 and completed in 2001 by a series of Action Plans. The Biodiversity Action Plan includes, among the actions necessary to support the Natura 2000 Network, Action 28 geared to 'enhancing (ecological) connectivity between Natura 2000 sites'. According to this document, ecological corridors should

8
Seven thematic strategies
The thematic strategies drawn up in the framework of the 6th Environment Action Programme 2002-2012 take a longer-term perspective and as their goal is to support sustainable development, they also provide a tool for the implementation of PEEN. The thematic strategies have been developed for the following fields:
• air pollution,
• prevention and recycling of waste,
• protection and conservation of the marine environment,
• soil,
• sustainable use of pesticides,
• sustainable use of resources,
• urban environment.

Other Community instruments conducive to establishing the Pan-European ecological network

Directives on the assessment of the impact of human activities on the environment

⑨ Coastal planning and integrated management

The coast, by its very nature, is an important corridor. The European Union has 38,000km of coastline and plays a major role in seeking to influence governments to improve protection of coastal habitats. The EU calls on the Member States to take a strategic, integrated approach to the management of their coastal areas in Recommendation no. 2002/413/EC. To this end, it suggested that the basis for such an approach should be coastal protection, economic and socio-cultural development and co-ordination. The Recommendation also included a series of principles to be observed, a description of national stocktaking procedures and suggested national strategies. The EU also supports pilot projects in this field.

The Maritime Strategy, currently under review, which aims to raise marine ecosystems to a good ecological state by 2021 will also be useful in protecting coastline corridors.

The process of assessing the effects of public and private projects on the environment makes it possible to gauge the impact of different actions on natural habitats. Assessments of this type are particularly significant where connectivity is concerned as they enable us to evaluate the effects of projects on the fragmentation of natural habitats. The Environmental Impact Assessment Directive (85/337/EEC) of 1985 set out the rules governing the assessment of the impacts of projects on humans, ecosystems and cultural sites. The need to broaden environmental assessment before projects are launched by extending it to policies, plans and programmes was enshrined in Community law in 2001 through the adoption of the Directive on strategic environmental assessment (SEA). This new Directive makes it possible to study the direct and indirect effects of policies, plans and programmes on natural habitats well before any procedures are set in motion and this could have a real positive effect on planning for maintenance of connectivity for nature. Although it is only an obligation as to means and not as to results, impact assessment is a measure for preventing damage to unprotected natural habitats. It is therefore a key instrument for integrating nature conservation into other policies.

Sectoral instruments

The Communication from the Commission of 13 December 2005 on the review of the Sustainable Development Strategy emphasizes the importance of integrating environmental concerns into sectoral policies. It points out that improved sustainable natural resource management is one of the European Union's objectives, that the link between economic growth and the use of such resources must be broken and that the loss of biodiversity must be halted by 2010.

Limiting the adverse effects of transport and correcting regional imbalances is another long-term objective. The European transport and environment strategy adopted in 2002 sets goals for the integration of environmental concerns into transport policy. It provides guidelines for a series of measures in the different transport sectors such as road, air, rail and sea transport. The strategy highlights the positive impact of some of the measures that have already been taken at EU level,

Cordier-Huguet

Mute swan

but it also insists on the need for continued effort in certain areas, particularly measures to counter the adverse effects of increases in traffic volume.

The European Union has also devised a strategic approach to integrate environmental issues into agricultural policy, particularly in the context of the various reforms of the CAP. Since the 1992 CAP reform environmental protection has been integrated in the CAP objectives. Agriculture depends on the availability of natural resources, and the use of these resources can put pressure on the environment. The varied landscapes and the associated biodiversity which have been shaped by agriculture over the centuries can be seriously affected by the intensification or abandonment of land use.

On the other hand farmers can help protect the environment by certain actions, for which purpose the agri-environmental measures have been put in place. Farmers who provide environmental benefits on a voluntary basis can now be remunerated. The Berlin Agreement of 1999 has recognized the multifunctionality of agriculture and has constructed the CAP on two 'pillars'. The 1st pillar concerns the support of production and the organisation of the market. The 2nd pillar contains support of rural development and other components of agriculture, including the environment. The Luxembourg Agreement of 2003 foresees a single payment system for farms, according to certain criteria relating to the environment, food safety and animal welfare. The goal of this reform is to guarantee that the agricultural sector complies with environmental standards in order to stimulate good agricultural practice at national level. This may provide a tool for corridor development in the rural environment.

EU forest management initiatives related to foresty are also steadily taking environmental considerations into account. The new Action Plan for sustainable forest management, adopted in June 2006, places protection and improvement of the environment among its four main objectives. In contrast to forest managed in an intensive manner the forests that are managed sustainably can in fact be used by a range of species as an ecological continuum. This new orientation of Community initiatives on forests may provide yet another tool for implementing PEEN.

10 PEEN and Community spatial planning policy

The European Spatial Development Perspective is a common reference framework adopted by the Ministers responsible for spatial planning in 1999. Its aim is to increase transnational consultation and co-operation on spatial planning issues. It states that sensitive areas should be developed in keeping with their ecological function. It also calls for the 'continued development of European ecological networks, as proposed by Natura 2000, including the necessary links between natural sites and protected areas of regional, national, transnational and EU-wide importance'. In so doing, it confirms the importance of the Pan-European Ecological Network and the need for spatial planners to take it into account.

11

Fish migration and the Directive establishing a framework for Community action in the field of water policy

The 2000 Water Framework Directive lays down guidelines on European water policy for the next few decades. Although it does not explicitly require Member States to restore the movement of migratory fish species, it does advocate ensuring that rivers and watercourses are in a *"very good state"*. Annex V to the Directive specifies the following precondition for the state of a river to qualify as being *"very good"*:

"the continuity of the river is not disturbed by anthropogenic activities and allows undisturbed migration of aquatic organisms and sediment transport".

In responding to the need to adopt a river catchment perspective, the Water Framework Directive situates management of aquatic ecosystems in the long term. Crucial to the conservation of biodiversity, the restoration and management actions foreseen by the Directive will also help in preventing floods. The Water Framework Directive therefore promotes the restoration of ecological connectivity, which is geared, among other things, to maintaining ecological processes in aquatic environments.

Contribution to the Pan-European ecological network by national and sub-national instruments

Assessing action to implement ecological networks at national and sub-national level enables us to gauge the knock-on effect of (and for) the Pan-European Biological and Landscape Diversity Strategy.

The potential to set up ecological networks and the challenges this poses may not be the same in Western European and Central and Eastern European countries (Council of Europe, 2003). In Western European countries, the deterioration of natural areas, population density and the fragmentation and isolation of natural habitats are such that establishing ecological networks often involves not only schemes to protect natural areas but also nature restoration programmes. This fact, which is characteristic of Western European countries, is particularly relevant to such countries as Belgium, Luxembourg and the Netherlands. In these countries the ecological networks comprise not only core areas and buffer zones but also nature development areas.

Overall European countries contribute to the establishment of PEEN through their own nature protection policies and specifically through the establishment of networks of protected areas. A growing number of countries have taken the next steps by

implementing nature protection policies which aim at effectively maintaining or restoring ecological connectivity either through governmental policies or nature protection laws. While some countries have chosen to integrate protection of ecological networks in nature policy law, others have chosen to identify biological interconnections in land-planning documents. Moreover, while some countries have chosen to implement ecological networks at national level, others have chosen sub-national levels to do so. All these examples point to a major political determination to combat the fragmentation of natural habitats.

Different types of legal text

Several countries have favoured integration of ecological networks in public policies without binding requirements. In April 1999, for instance, the Luxembourg Government Council adopted a National Plan for Sustainable Development. This governmental plan stipulates that the preservation of biological diversity must have equal priority status with other land-use interests and be an integral part of government programmes and policies. The Government set the major aim of creating a National Biodiversity Network made up of two networks of protected areas to be gradually interlinked with ecological corridors. In Kyrgyzstan the Strategy and Action Plan for the conservation of biodiversity, published in 1998 provide for the establishment of an ecological network. To reach this goal an ecological code was launched by the government in 2004. The Netherlands drew up a specific nature conservation document, the Nature Management Plan, in November 1990. This plan provided for the installation of a national ecological network over the following 30 years. The new Plan adopted in July 2000 under the title 'Nature for People, People for Nature' pursues the same goal. The text endeavours to combat the fragmentation and isolation of natural habitats and also to co-ordinate existing legal instruments relating to nature conservation.

Other countries have used legal channels to implement ecological networks on their territory. In Hungary the legal basis for the creation of the National Ecological Network was the 1996 Nature Conservation Act, No. LIII. This Act singles out implementation of a national ecological network as an important objective in the National Programme for the Environment. It also defines the ecological network as a network of protected areas, buffer

Shepherd (HU)

zones and peripheral areas. The core areas in the network must be fully protected by the end of 2008. However, pending publication of an implementing decree, the protection of natural habitats outside the protected areas is under pressure owing to conflicts between conservation and economic interests. In the Former Yougoslav Republic of Macedonia, a national ecological network within the meaning of PEEN has not yet been established

yet. But, its development is planned in the new Law on Nature Protection (Official Gazette No. 67/2004) and in the National Biodiversity Strategy and Action Plan (adopted in 2004).

Recognition of ecological networks in binding instruments, and of the concept itself in particular, is important but it does not ensure the effectiveness of the network. Promoting the concept through governmental instruments can also support ecological connectivity of territories. However, beyond instruments as such, which vary according to the legal traditions of each country, political support for the implementation of ecological networks is crucial.

Different levels of implementation

In Belgium, the Flemish Region's ecological network, known as the 'Principal Ecological Structure', was legally established under the Decree of 21 October 1997 on the conservation of nature and the natural environment. This legislative document lays the legal foundations at the federal level for creating this network, which is based on two different systems of zones. The Flemish ecological network breaks down into two subsets: the VEN (*Vlaams Ecologisch Netwerk* – *Flemish* ecological network), which concerns the core areas, and the IVON (*Integraal Verwevings- en Ondersteunend Netwerk* – 'integrated supportive network'), which comprises buffer zones and ecological corridors. According to the Plan for the Flemish 'Principal Ecological Structure', 125,000ha of VEN and 150,000ha of IVON are to be designated by 2007. The development plans for VEN zones and IVON buffer zones must be drawn up by 2008.

Conversely, in Germany, creation of ecological networks has been decided upon at federal level. The ecological network concept was included in the German Nature Conservation Act adopted in 2002, although its implementation is a matter for the federated States *(Länder)*. Article 3 of the Federal Nature Conservation Act sets out the legal foundation for creating ecological networks throughout the Federal Territory. This legislation sets two complementary objectives: conserving native species and their habitats and biotic communities, and conserving, restoring and developing functional ecological relations. Each *Land* is required to create an ecological network covering 10% of its territory. The *Land* must also guarantee network coherence beyond its boundaries. The networks have been or are being created in all 16 *Länder*.

Switzerland launched the preparatory work on its 'Swiss Landscape' Concept in 1992 (CPS), which

Grey lag goose, Flanders (B)

lays down the basis for an ecological network at Federal level. It was approved by the Federal Council in 1997. The CPS also includes sectoral objectives intended to 'minimise the biologically divisive effects of present or future transport infrastructures', to adapt watercourses to the free movement of fish and to develop riverbanks as corridors for small land animals. Lastly, the Confederation sets the aim of promoting the networking of biotopes by introducing biological corridors and 'relay biotopes' at regional or local level, particularly by means of hydrographical networks.

The importance of this distinction is relative because to be operational these national ecological networks have to be implemented at local level and eventually the different ecological networks developed at regional level will have to reach a common approach.

Different fields of implementation

The effectiveness of the methods chosen for creating eco-corridors at national and sub-national level depends on the practices and traditions of each country. Most of the countries which have used the ecological stability approach have first sought to protect ecological networks through spatial planning documents and then adopted nature protection documents. On the other hand, most Western European countries which have set up policies to protect ecological networks began by integrating the concept into legislation on nature protection and are now beginning to ensure that it is taken into account in spatial planning documents.

Viviparous lizard

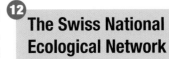

The Swiss National Ecological Network

The national ecology network, Switzerland's contribution to the PEEN indicative map, was implemented in conjunction with the cantonal departments for nature and landscape protection. It is a technical and scientific report (2004) setting out an ecology-based vision of the landscape for the entire territory of Switzerland, indicating the fragmentation and inter-connection of key areas, both existing and potential, on national maps on scales of 1:500 000 and 1:100 000. This overarching, forward-looking vision reveals the broad outlines planned for Switzerland's major ecology networks. Complementing the management of remarkable and threatened species and biotopes, the national ecology network provides a basis for a policy of revitalising key areas and an incentive for a new form of partnership at all levels, with the sectors concerned by landscape management, such as transport and communications, agriculture and forestry, water conservation, national security, territorial development, and also hunting, fishing and nature and landscape protection.

The Czech Republic and Slovakia have recognized the importance of ecological networks through their nature protection laws. The territorial system for ecological stability which was developed in Czechoslovakia in the 1980s formed an integral part of a system that involved planning in all fields. Following the political division of the country, the two successor States, the Czech Republic and Slovakia, retained this system. The Czech ecological network was set up under the Nature and Landscape Protection Act, No. 117/92 of 19 February 1992, which defines the ecological stability system as a complex of interconnected natural or semi-natural ecosystems geared to guaranteeing natural ecological stability. The system is seen as counterbalancing any attacks on the environment from agricultural and industrial activities. Contracts or land exchange agreements can be concluded with landowners in order to gain their support for the territorial system for ecological stability. The flooding that occurred at the beginning of this millennium has apparently revived the process of implementing the territorial system for ecological stability, considered as legally in the public interest.

In France, the 1999 Sustainable Spatial Planning (General Principles) Act (loi d'orientation) was the first to legally recognise the concept of ecological network. This piece of legislation stipulates that the Collective Services Plan for Natural and Rural Areas must identify 'the ecological networks, continuities and extensions of protected areas to be organized'. This Act does not, however, mention protecting or managing such areas, and in practical terms identification involves no other obligation than drawing up an inventory of the areas.

The Collective Services Plan for Natural and Rural Areas provides that *"the existence in the national territory of an ecological network within a European framework by 2020 is a fundamental objective of the policy to protect biodiversity (...)."*

The Plan specifies that the ecological network to be created must be operational, i.e. it must *"guarantee continuity between all officially identified sites of major ecological interest and attain the desired aim of protecting species and reacting effectively to any environmental disasters or problems of climate change."*

The creation of ecological networks by an increasing number of local authorities demonstrates the impact of the Plan.

In Estonia, there are several pieces of legislation geared to protecting ecological corridors. The 1997 National Strategy for the Environment and the 1998 National Action Plan for the Environment both identify the creation of the ecological network as a priority objective for 2010. The Sustainable Development Act also refers to the national ecological network, as does the Urban Development and Spatial Planning Act (1995). The National Spatial Planning Strategy specifies the objectives in terms of wildlife and landscape protection, the ecological network is described as being made up of major core areas with narrow interconnecting corridors. The actions set out in the Strategy expressly include identifying areas of conflict between the green network and the transport network.

Planning documents must be drawn up to guarantee passageways for animals in these areas of conflicting interests.

While some countries have chosen to establish ecological networks by legislation, the concept of ecological network can also act as a bridge between nature protection legislation and land planning within a sustainable development context. Taking into account ecological networks within land planning schemes appears to be crucial for long term maintenance of natural infrastructures.

It is difficult to assess the positive effects of either approaches as in most cases it is necessary to combine them for an effective result. As such the concept of ecological network is a tool to de-compartmentalise public policies.

Conclusion

At international and European levels a large number of policies and laws form the basis for creating the Pan-European Ecological Network. In the last decade, especially since the adoption of PEBLDS in 1995, increasing numbers of countries have adopted ecological network protection policies and legislation. A move towards implementation is noticed in a number of countries.

The fact that the importance of biological interconnections is now mentioned in legal texts at all decision-making levels proves that there is a solid legal basis for the Pan-European Ecological Network. The European framework is being gradually transposed at national and sub-national levels, each level with its own tools and instruments that best fit local conditions and needs. PEEN also provides a framework making for coherence between each of these instruments. By participating in this Pan-European initiative, the States will also be honouring their international obligations in a highly practical way.

*Ysyk-Kol lake,
Kirghizistan*

P. Thébault

CHAPTER
III

Progress on implementation in Europe :
functioning ecological networks

Irish shores, Co. Antrin

The ecological
network concept

i s occupying an increasingly important place in scientific research, policy-making and legislation, and the practical implementation of PEEN is steadily taking shape. This is happening through a combination of initiatives at various levels: at Pan-European level, at national level and at local level. In all cases, co-operation among authorities beyond administrative boundaries as well as adequate financial means are key drivers of PEEN's success.

This chapter aims to establish the extent to which various components of PEEN are operational throughout Europe, i.e. are contributing to the maintenance or restoration of ecological connectivity and resilience on a Pan-European scale. In this sense, this chapter is a first attempt at assessing the current state of affairs on the ground concerning the establishment of a Pan-European Ecological Network.

For the purposes of this assessment, it was necessary to give substance to the concepts of 'core areas' and 'corridors', used in the theoretical approach to PEEN, by translating them into terms that can be evaluated (i.e. empirical) and are preferably spatial. To this end the following pragmatic operational definitions were applied:

Core areas

An area identified as a potential pan-European core area is able to function as such if it has been designated under international instruments and/or is a large area designated under national instruments with provisions for nature conservation.

Corridors

Corridors are sections of land facilitating ecological connectivity between the core areas. A specific section of land/water identified as a potential pan-European corridor is assumed to be able to function as a corridor if one or more of the following qualifications apply:
• covered by national designations;
• covered by high nature value farmland;
• covered by sustainably managed forests;
• natural river;
• natural coastline;
• part of an operational national or regional ecological network.

In order to assess the state of affairs concerning the PEEN core areas, the following sections provide an overview of the state of implementation throughout Europe of various international legal and policy instruments aiming to designate natural areas of international or European importance.

To assess the state of affairs concerning the corridors, a review is provided of the state of implementation of national, transboundary or regional ecological networks. In addition to physical implementation on the ground various forms of transboundary co-operation are reviewed, developments in policies related to crucial sectors such as agriculture, forestry, water management and spatial planning are considered and an indication is given of funding instruments in relation to establishing ecological networks.

Progress made in the Pan-European ecological network zones

Protection of core and buffer zones

One of the main features of nature conservation policies has, from the beginning, been the designation of protected areas. The first nature reserves in Europe were created in 1895 in Slovakia (Ponicka Dubrav and Priloj). Since then, every country has devised its own classification system, ranging from strict protection regimes, as in the case of strict nature reserves or some national parks, to less stringent protection types, such as landscape parks, or the targeted and systematic protection of certain habitats or ecosystems. The introduction of international and European regulations on nature conservation and biodiversity has encouraged countries to take coordinated action to identify and solve the chief problems of conservation supranationally. This has led to the setting-up of various networks of protected sites, each serving a specific purpose, but complementing one another in pursuing the central aim of preserving biodiversity.

All these protected areas, whether organized in coordinated networks or not, prefigure the Pan-European Ecological Network, not only as core – and sometimes buffer – areas, but also as the expression of a political determination to conserve nature, and as an institutional framework for doing so. These networks facilitate exchange of related techniques and expertise.

The Natura 2000 Network

Comprising Special Protection Areas under the EC Birds Directive, and Special Areas of Conservation under the EC Habitats Directive, the Natura 2000 Network makes a crucial contribution to protection of the core areas in the Pan-European Ecological Network.

Progress in fulfilling the objectives of the Natura 2000 Network is assessed through various steps. The first phase of implementation has focused on proposal and designation by EU Member States of sites holding species and habitats of European interest. The degree of completeness of the national proposals is expressed, in the case of the Habitats Directive, by the *"Site Proposal Sufficiency Index"*.

The next steps in implementing the Natura 2000 Network will aim to establish the operational character of the Network, to ensure in particular that species and habitats of European importance are maintained in a favourable conservation status. One of the Member States' priorities is establishing the necessary conservation measures, including preparing management plans and adapting appropriate national statutory, administrative or contractual measures.

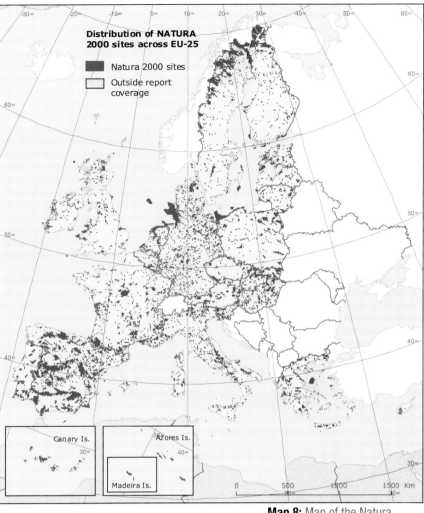

Map 8: Map of the Natura 2000 Network; September 2006. Source: EC-DG Environment, ETC/BD

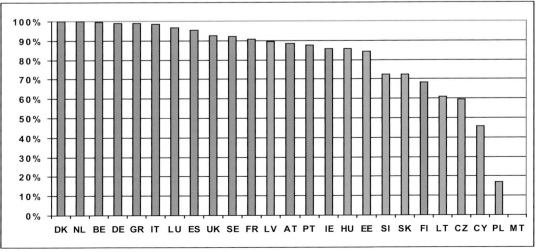

Figure 2: State of progress by member states in reaching sufficient sites proposals for Annex I habitats and Annex II species under the Habitats Directive, September 2006. Source: EC-DG Environment, ETC/BD.

Against the background of global climate change and changes in land use, the Network's ability to achieve its conservation objectives depends, inter alia, on the maintenance or restoration of a suitable matrix of land within and between sites conducive to maintaining essential ecological processes and supporting

Wild boar family (CH)

biodiversity. In accordance with Article 10 of the Habitats Directive, the European Commission and some Member States are currently attempting to identify the necessary conditions and resources in order to ensure coherent management of landscape features throughout the Natura 2000 Network.

The Natura 2000 Network does not merely bring potential core areas to PEEN; it is a living example of an EU-wide ecological net-work-building process. By involving a huge number of stakeholders – owners and occu-piers of land, local, national and European authorities – across all sectors, the Natura 2000 Network aims at ensuring biodiversity conservation beyond national boundaries while at the same time maintaining dynamic rural areas. The principle of collaboration is enshrined in the Habitats Directive, which requires that conservation measures *"take account of economic, social and cultural re-quirements and the regional and local char-acteristics of the area"*.

As of June 2006, the Natura 2000 Network comprises 20,582 sites under the Habitats Directive, including 1,250 marine sites (12% of the area of the European Union), and 4,317 sites under the Birds Directive, including 459 marine sites (9% of the area of the European Union).

The Emerald Network

Set up under the Bern Convention but also open to 'observer countries' to this Convention, the Emerald Network – envisaged as early as 1989 – was given practical form in 1996 by the Standing Committee to the Bern Convention with a view to supplementing the Natura 2000 Network, on a similar basis, in non-Community countries, based on the highest possible methodological synergy. As well as helping to identify and conserve core areas of the Pan-European Ecological Network, the Emerald Network, which is in the process of being developed, also facilitates the establishment of national networks of protected areas. As the European Union is also a Contracting Party to the Bern Convention, Natura 2000 is considered to be the EU contribution to the Emerald Network.

For Bern Convention Contracting Parties which are European Union Member States, the Emerald Network sites consist of the Natura 2000 sites. Before joining the European Union, twelve countries have implemented Emerald pilot projects as preparatory work to setting up the Natura 2000 network. The other countries engaged in the constitution of the Emerald Network are : in Western Europe, Iceland, Norway, Switzerland, in Central and Eastern Europe, Moldova, the Federation of Russia and Ukraine, in South-Eastern and and East Europe, Albania, Bosnia-Herzegovina, Croatia, Montenegro, "The former Yugoslav Republic of Macedonia", Serbia, Turkey, and in the South Caucasus, Armenia, Azerbaijan and Georgia.

An ambitious Emerald Network development programme was implemented in 2005/2006, in South-Eastern Europe, as a continuation of the initial pilot projects implemented by the Council of Europe. This CARDS/Emerald programme concerns the following countries: Albania, Bosnia-Herzegovina, Croatia, Montenegro, "the Former Yugoslav Republic of Macedonia" and Serbia. Its overall objective is to identify 80 % of the sites in these countries. The programme benefits from a financial contribution of the European Environmental Agency and represents an important tool contributing to preparing the countries concerned for the future work on Natura 2000 and for advance compliance with the Habitats and Birds Directives.

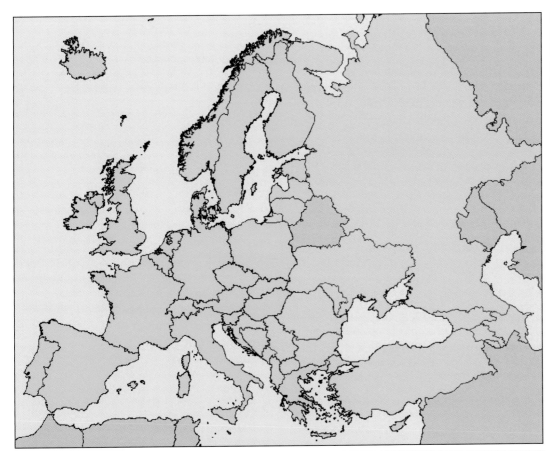

Map 9: Map of the countries which implement the Natura 2000 network and the Emerald Network. Source: ETC/BD, 2006.

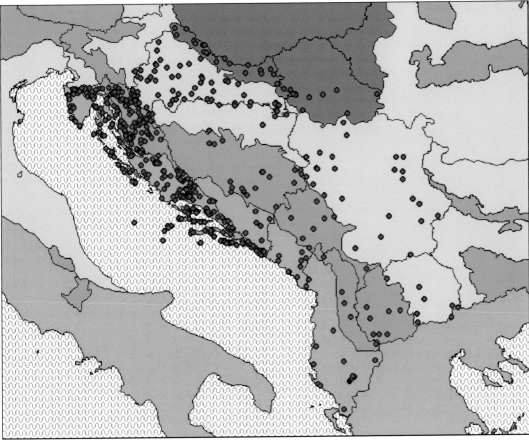

Map 10: Sites proposed under the Emerald pilot projects in the countries of South-Eastern Europe, June 2006. Source: ETC/BD.

Twenty-eight pilot projects have been implemented or are currently organized with a view to launching the Emerald Network, of which 21 in Central and Eastern Europe and South Caucasus.

13 Emerald Network pilot project in Azerbaidjan

The Republic of Azerbaijan signed the Bern Convention in March 2000, and is now preparing to set up the Emerald Network on its territory. A team of experts has identified 21 types of endangered natural habitats within the meaning of Resolution No. 4 (1996) of the Standing Committee to the Bern Convention. Azerbaijan wishes to take the work done further by devising a national strategy and action plan for biological diversity, as well as establishing the national ecological network.

Other networks of protected areas in Europe

In addition to the Natura 2000 and Emerald Networks, several other networks of protected sites are in place within Europe as a whole. Stemming from international or regional arrangements, each of these networks has a specific background and purpose, ranging from protection of exceptional heritage sites to conservation of sites of high ecological and functional value, or sites dedicated to scientific research and sustainable development. They all contribute to better conservation of natural habitats throughout Europe.

Conservation and protection of outstanding areas

WORLD HERITAGE

On account of their exceptional nature, the World Heritage sites designated under the 1972 World Heritage Convention for their outstanding natural or landscape value contribute to establishment of core areas in the Pan-European Ecological Network.

As of 2006, 79 World Heritage sites had been designated for their natural or landscape value in 49 European countries, parties to the Convention.

EUROPEAN DIPLOMA

The 'European Diploma of Protected Areas' aims to reward exemplary management of natural or semi-natural areas or landscapes of exceptional European interest for conservation of biological, geological and landscape diversity. The concept of exemplary management introduces an important management dynamic for these core areas of the Pan-European Ecological Network. The diploma is awarded on the basis of a site's ecological quality and European interest as well as its legal protection status. The objective of nature conservation is pursued by awarding an honorary distinction, making it possible to develop a network of sites designated by the Council of Europe.

As of 2006, the European Diploma had been awarded to 66 sites in 25 countries.

Map 11: Sites which have been awarded the European Diploma of protected areas, Source: CTE/BD, 2005.

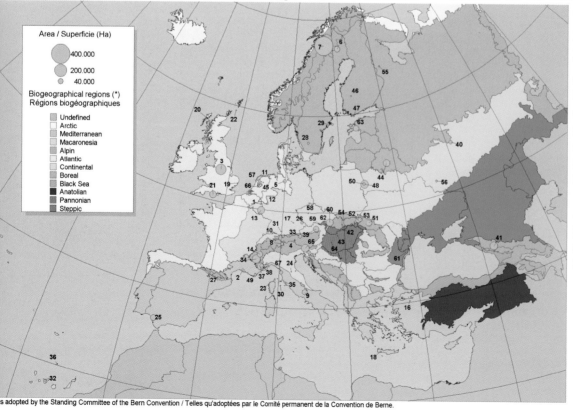

Conservation of nature areas where the ecological stakes are high

RAMSAR SITES

The network of Ramsar sites aims to protect a type of ecosystem that is particularly rich biologically, but also under considerable threat worldwide. These Ramsar sites play a crucial role in protecting waterfowl migration routes and in the proper management of the ecological processes and services provided by wetlands. They thereby help establishing a coherent spatial structure playing a particular role in preventing floods and mitigating the effects of pollution, thus coinciding with the sustainable development objectives of the Pan-European Ecological Network.

Map 12: Map of Ramsar sites in Europe, 2006. Source: Wetlands International

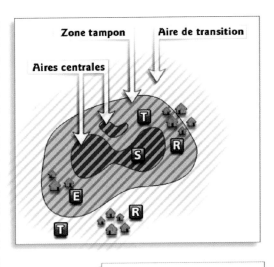

Biosphere Reserves fit in well with ecological networks since they combine conservation of resources with sustainable development. For this purpose, they are divided into three zones: a core zone whose legal status must ensure long-term protection, and where most human activities are prohibited; a clearly defined buffer zone, where only activities compatible with conservation are permitted; and a transitional zone, which does not usually have protected status, and which permits and promotes sustainable use of resources.

Increasingly, the Biosphere Reserves are seeking to establish ecological networks within their sites.

As of 2006, there were 193 Biosphere Reserves in 31 European and Central Asian countries.

Figure 3 : Organising scheme of Biosphere Reserves. Source: Unesco.

Sustainable development and scientific research

BIOSPHERE RESERVES

Biosphere Reserves have three functions which are clearly defined, complementary and of equal importance: a conservation function (to preserve genetic resources, spaces and ecosystems, and landscapes), a development function (to promote sustainable economic and human development), and a logistical function (to permit and encourage research, permanent surveillance, education and training).

BIOGENETIC RESERVES

The Network of Biogenetic Reserves, started by the Council of Europe, is designed to encourage Member States to co-operate with a view to conserving representative examples of natural habitats that are especially valuable for nature conservation in Europe. The Network was set up on this basis, which explains the dual objective of Biogenetic Reserves: to guarantee the biological balance and conservation of representative examples of European heritage, and to provide a field of research for finding out how ecosystems function and evolve.

As of 2006, there were 376 Biogenetic Reserves in 23 European countries

Networks of protected areas at national level

Independently of the European and international designations in application, each country has set up its own protection instruments over the years. And so, throughout Europe, there are nearly 800 different designation types corresponding to over 75,000 nationally protected sites.

The aims of designation vary greatly, ranging from strict protection of a natural area (national parks, nature reserves) to the regulation of human activities (hunting reserves, landscape protection, and regulated forest management). This being so, all of the 75,000 nationally protected sites contribute to PEEN as core areas, buffer zones and even corridors.

Moreover, separately or in conjunction, national designations often – but not systematically – support designation within a European or international context. Thus a Natura 2000 site may combine a nature reserve already designated at national level, a State-owned forest and a hunting reserve.

The area of nationally protected areas is increasing steadily (Figure 3.6).

Table 1:

Examples of national designation types:

PORTUGAL	AUSTRIA
Designation types used with the intention to protect fauna, flora, habitats and landscapes (the latter as far as relevant for fauna, flora and for habitat protection)	
Reserva integral	Nationalpark
Reserva Botânica	Naturpark
Reserva Zoológica	Naturshutzgebeit
Area Ornitológica de Recuperação	Landschaftsschutzgebeit
	Geschütztes Biotop (only in Vienna)
	Europaschutzgebiet (= Natura 2000 site)
	Biosphärenpark (= Biosphere Reserve)
Parque Nacional	Ruhegebeit
Reserva Natural	Geschützter Landschaftsteil
Parque Natural	Geschützte Grünbestände
Sítio Classificado	Geschützte Naturgebilde von örtlicher Bedeutung
Paisagem Protegida	Sonstige Landschaftsteile
	Naturdenkmal
	Naturhölen
	Baumschutz (in der Stadt Salzburg)
	Moorschutz
	Feuchtgebietsschutz
	Auwaldschutz
	Schutz stehender Gewässer (einschließlich Uferbereich)
	Schutz fließender Gewässer (einschließlich Uferbereich)
	Schutz der Gletscher
	Schutz der Alpinregion (bzw. D. Alpinen Ödlandes)
	Seltene und bedrochte Tiertaren (aufgeslistet) sowie deren Lebensräume
	Pilze
Status categories under sectoral, legislative and administrative acts, particularly forestry, providing adequate protection for fauna, flora and habitat conservation	
Reserva Ecólogica Nacional	Naturwaldzellen (Forstrecht)
Domínio Público Hídrico	Erholungswald (Forstrecht)
Reserva Agrícola Nacional	Schutzwald ((Forstrecht)
Mata Nacional	Wasserschutzgebiete (Wasserrecht)
Reserva Florestal Natural Integral	Wasserschöngebiete (Wasserrecht)
Reserva Florestal Natural Parcial	Ökologish besonders wertwolle Gebiete (Raumordnung)
Reserva Florestal de Recreio	Habitatschutzgebiet (Jagdrecht)
Locais de Caça Prohibida	Wild-Europaschutzgebiet (Jagdrecht, only in Salzburg)
Zona de Pesca Reservada	
Zona de Defesa e Controlo Urbano	
Zona de Pesca Condicionada	
Zona de Abrigo	
Zona de Desova	
Zona de Pesca Profissional	
Concessões de Pesca Deportiva	
Perímetro Florestal	
Reserva de Caça Integral	
Reserva de Caça Parcial	
Zona de Caça de Interesse Municipal	
Zona de Caça de Interesse Turistico	
Zona de Caça de Interesse Associativo	
Zona de Direito à Não Caça	
Private status categories providing sustainable protection for fauna, flora and habitat conservation	
Sitio de Interesse Biológico	Moorerhaltungsprämien (zumeist in Feuchtgebieten)
	Beweidungsprämien (zumeist in Halbtrockenrasen oder Almbereich)
	Lärchenwiesenprämien (zur Erhaltung der tradinonellen Kulturform Lärchenwiese)
	Düngeverzichtsprämien (zumeist in Feuchtgebieten und Halbtrockenrasen)
	Almberwirtschaftungsprämien
	Prämien fur Au ernutzungstellung von ökol. wertvollen

Use of sectoral policies in developing corridors

European landscapes, with all their biodiversity, have been fashioned by thousands of years of human activity. They are now under threat from increasing fragmentation, a combination of urbanisation and ever greater spread of transport infrastructures, and also increasingly specialised intensive agricultural practices.

Incorporating environmental considerations into sectoral policies does, however, provide opportunities for restoring conditions favourable to biodiversity, particularly by creating ecological corridors (Klemm, 1992). New schemes may thus allow defragmentation of natural habitats e.g. by restoring free watercourse movement, rehabilitating fauna mobility across motorways by means of eco-bridges, preserve extensive farming

14
The network of nationally protected areas in Georgia

Georgia established the first nature reserve – the Lagodekhi Strict Nature Reserve – in the Caucasus in 1912. Its network of nationally protected areas now comprises 18 nature reserves with a total area of 171,903 hectares, and four national parks with a total area of 210,843 hectares. It has also protected 11 sanctuaries, three with extensive buffer zones. While current protected areas are still insufficient to preserve the country's biodiversity, the Georgian Government has indicated that it wishes to bring 15% of forests into these areas.

Figure 4: Acumulated area of nationally designated zones in 30 European countries for the period 1900-2004. Source: ETC/BD-UNEP-WCMC-CoE

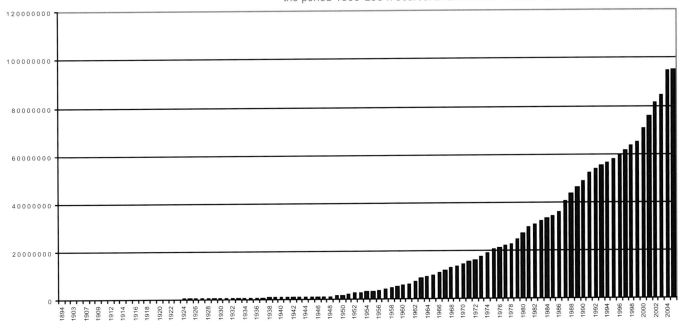

systems and replant hedgerows in intensive single-cropping landscapes (Council of Europe, 2000/2). Above and beyond traditional nature conservation methods based on protected areas, these sectoral policies are vital instruments for the development of the Pan-European Ecological Network.

Corridors for and through sustainable agriculture and forestry

Maintenance or establishment of ecological corridors through farming and forestry practices relates not only to linear elements such as hedges, wooded paths and streams or 'grassy edges of crop fields', but also to larger extensively-managed areas which allow foraging, reproduction and dispersal of wildlife between core protected areas.

*Establishment of corridors
via sustainable farming policies*

The reforms of agricultural policies which have been carried out at Community level as well as in most European countries are

Figure 5: Ecological importance of linear elements in rural landscapes. Source: Arbres et Paysages, 32..

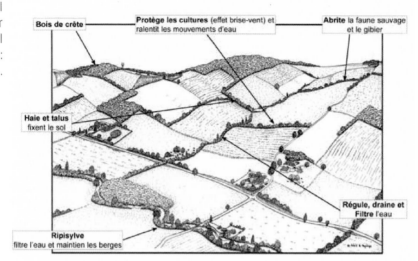

part of a general trend towards making the nature and landscape conservation objective an important component of sectoral policies, as reflected in the final declaration of the Pan-European Conference 'Towards integration of biological and landscape diversity for sustainable agriculture in Europe' organized by the Council of Europe and Unesco in Paris, 2002 (Council of Europe, 2003/3). This integration is achieved in various ways:

AGRI-ENVIRONMENTAL MEASURES

Agri-environmental measures were introduced into Community law in the 1980s at the initiative of the United Kingdom. These measures are designed to encourage farmers to protect and enhance the environment on their land. Some of these measures relate to preservation of landscape and historical features such as hedgerows, ditches and

woods, management of low-intensity pasture systems, conservation of high-value habitats and the biodiversity they hold.

In this respect they are a useful means of encouraging the creation of biological corridors on farmland. Many countries have also introduced measures, together with or separately from Community regulations, geared to preserving biodiversity on agricultural land.

In Denmark, planting and maintaining hedges are almost entirely traditional activities. Hedge-planting subsidies ensure that long linear elements (approximately 20 km) can be installed and that the planting process is organized collectively. One of the reasons for the success of this system is certainly the high level of public funding available, covering up to 70% of the hedge-planting costs. In the United Kingdom, subsidies are available not only for planting hedges but also for hedgerow improvements, e.g. by diversifying the species planted and using special hedge-trimming techniques. This is particularly important in the case of those habitats that require human maintenance. Such measures facilitate the protection and restoration of a wide range of biological interconnections. Nevertheless, the measures must be part of an overall connectivity rationale if they are to be genuinely operational.

ECO-CONDITIONALITY OF SUBSIDIES

Key to the 2003 reform of the Common Agricultural Policy, 'eco-conditionality' may provide opportunities to improve the agricultural matrix of European territory for biodiversity and therefore contribute to PEEN. It brings a radical change in the way European subsidies are allocated. Eco-conditionality relates to the first pillar of the CAP, which deals with market and prices support, while the second pillar of the CAP relates to rural development. The agreement reached by Ministers for Agriculture in Luxembourg in 2003 stipulates that all EU agricultural subsidies (direct payments) will henceforth be conditional upon compli-

Squirrels' protection (UK)

ance with environmental standards. Eco-conditionality compels farmers to meet legal obligations such as the Birds and the Habitats Directives, as well as to maintain land in good agricultural and environmental conditions. Each Member State is free to decide on the means it wishes to use to apply eco-conditionality. These may include hedge planting as well as establishment of 'grassy edges of crop fields' which act as a buffer between agricultural lands and rivers, therefore mitigating pollution and erosion effects.

MULTIFUNCTIONALITY IN AGRICULTURE AND RURAL DEVELOPMENT

Recent reforms of agricultural policy have introduced a new approach to agricultural objectives whereby each production goal is twinned with an environmental objective, so that agriculture now has both an ecological and a productive function. The European Union's rural development policy is designed to ensure the harmonious development of rural areas on the basis of this agricultural multifunctionality. Aimed not only at farmers stricto sensu, this policy attempts to reconcile the different modes of land use with a view to establishing a coherent framework for reinforcing the economic and social fabric of country areas, curbing rural depopulation, and maintaining and developing employment while encouraging a more environmentally friendly form of agriculture.

Many countries now acknowledge the multifunctional role of agriculture. In Switzerland, the concept of agricultural multifunctionality has been incorporated into the Constitution by referendum, which has facilitated citizen participation and therefore heightened public awareness. Swiss agriculture is now geared to guaranteeing food supplies for the population but also to contributing to the conservation of resources and the upkeep of the rural landscape. The federal law on agriculture stipulates that *"the Confederation encourages the conservation of the natural wealth of species, as a complement to the federal law on protection of nature and the landscape"*. The emergence of the concept of agricultural multifunctionality has prompted substantial progress in 'environmentalising' agricultural policy and is encouraging the introduction of numerous biological corridors in the farming environment.

The concept of High Nature Value Farming Areas (HNVFA) fits in with this multifunctional rationale by acknowledging the importance to European biodiversity of such specific agricultural habitats as permanent meadows and extensive fruit plantations. Several such areas have been incorporated into the Natura 2000 network on the basis of their exceptional animal and plant diversity. However, High Nature Value Farming Areas extend far beyond such protected areas. The need to identify and take account of HNVFAs in farming methods has been confirmed on the political front at both the Pan-European level (the Kyiv Resolution on Biodiversity) and within the European Union (EC Communication on Biodiversity, May 2006).

Establishment of corridors through sustainable forestry policies

Sustainable forest management is of major significance for the implementation of the Pan-European Ecological Network (Council of Europe, 2005). More and more international and national programmes are being launched and also smaller-scale ventures by individual farms, to encourage the sustainable management of woodlands, using methods which incorporate the ecological connectivity rationale.

Hurricane Lothar, December 1999

V. Munier

MINISTERIAL CONFERENCES ON THE PROTECTION OF FORESTS IN EUROPE (MCPFE)

In 1990 an initiative was launched for the protection of forests in Europe. This initiative, which includes regular ministerial conferences, highlights the strong commitment of the European States to promoting a sustainable, environmentally friendly forestry policy. At the close of the Vienna Conference in 2003, the European Ministers responsible for forestry from 40 different European countries approved a declaration and five resolutions

objectives in the management of forestry resources. And in Finland a new Forestry Act was adopted in 1996, followed by the Sustainable Forestry (Financing) Act in 1997.

The biotope interconnectivity rationale was incorporated into several provisions of the new Forestry Act, including one on the conservation of riverbanks, grassy forest edges and small water areas.

15

Towards a sustainable forestry policy in Russia

With over 850 million hectares of forest and 80,000 million cubic metres of timber, Russia has the largest forestry resources of any country in the world. A new partnership has been set up aimed at woodland conservation, with the support of IUCN. This project is geared to improving democratic management in the field of woodland conservation, establishing a participatory framework for managing forests in Russia and creating new sources of income by harvesting and marketing non-ligneous forestry products.

The Russian Office of the Forest Stewardship Council promotes voluntary forest certification in collaboration with the RF Forest Agency and the National Working Group for FSC-certification. As of 1 January 2007, 289 million hectares of Intact Forest Landscape have been identified, mapping of High Conservation Value Forests of other categories is in progress, and several HCVF belong to certified forest areas covering 13 million hectares.

concerning actions to promote the protection and sustainable development of forests in Europe.

The fifth Ministerial Conference on 'An Environment for Europe' (Kyiv, 2003) adopted a 'framework for co-operation' between the MCPFE and the Pan-European Biological and Landscape Diversity Strategy. The combination of these two initiatives confirms, in particular, the importance of the sustainable management of European forests for the implementation of the Pan-European Ecological Network.

CORRIDORS IN NATIONAL FORESTRY POLICIES

At the national level, reforms of forestry policies, like those of agricultural policies, have facilitated the incorporation of biodiversity protection into economic production goals. In Sweden, for instance, where forestry production is extremely important, the 1993 Forestry Act grants equal priority to ecological and production

ECO-CERTIFICATION OF WOODS

The development of eco-certification of woods helps forestry production systems to take account of biodiversity.

Changing forestry production methods can help maintain biological corridors in logging areas. For instance, during a clear-cutting operation it is possible to maintain wooded strips to facilitate dispersal of animals unable to circulate in open habitats. Conversely, open spaces can be regularly cleared in dense forests to facilitate the movement of species that require open areas in which to move. Moreover, many insect species and fungi depend on deadwood for their survival. Some of the specifications issued by forest eco-certification bodies require the maintenance of a specific minimum number of dead trees per hectare and the preservation of wooded or clear strips for the purposes of animal transit. Various forest eco-certification systems are now being established in Europe, thus contributing to the gradual establishment of

Deadwood (CH)

the Pan-European Ecological Network via sectoral policies.

Transport infrastructure and ecological infrastructure

There are frequent conflicts between wildlife and transport infrastructures. One of the best-known problems is the risk of collisions between animals and vehicles. The earliest measures taken in this field were therefore geared to reducing this risk by confining transport infrastructures to areas inaccessible to animals, especially large mammal species. However, this

16

The code of good practice for transport

In 1998 the Council of Europe drew up a code of practice, with a view to integrating biological and landscape considerations in the transport sector in the context of PEBLDS. This code is aimed at elected representatives, practitioners and decision-makers, and is intended to make them aware of the environmental dimension in planning and using transport networks (Council of Europe, 2001).

The code was presented in Kyiv in May 2003 at the fifth ministerial conference 'An Environment for Europe'.

has reduced wildlife mobility, and indeed often made it impossible for animals to overcome the obstacles of motorways or railways.

Loss of habitat is one of the main direct effects of road and rail transport infrastructures on the natural environment. Such loss may take on different forms depending on the type of infrastructure and species. The usually temporary loss of habitats during the construction phase differs from the complete loss of habitats situated along the planned route of the infrastructure and the type of loss caused by disturbances created when the infrastructure is put into service. The separation effect, also known as the barrier effect, arises from the dividing up of contiguous habitats during the construction of the infrastructure. The separation effect occurs where animals are unable to cross the infrastructure with ease because of fencing, physical installations or traffic flow.

MITIGATING THE CUT-OFF EFFECT, AND DEVELOPING WILDLIFE PATHWAYS

Wildlife pathways began to emerge roughly when the need to protect the environment became apparent. The first such pathways were built in the early 1970s.

There are different sorts of wildlife pathways, which vary in size and degree of effectiveness. 'Eco-bridges' up to 100 metres in width are nowadays being built across motorways, and on a smaller scale, some municipalities block local roads at night so that amphibians, for example, can cross safely.

Major road infrastructures can reduce the genetic variability of a given fauna population, cut off a vital part of a given population's living space, or prevent them from colonising new habitats. Taking account of these effects has been a gradual process, mainly driven by the desire to limit collisions between vehicles and wild mammals. Whereas the first wildlife pathways were usually too small and in the wrong places, the facilities are now much better suited to the needs of the animals in question.

Dangerous crossing (S)

Wildlife pathways can be installed ex post facto, in which case the aim is to *"restore continuity from a situation of discontinuity"*. Some countries have introduced environmental defragmentation programmes

Pathway (2006) near Eindhoven (NL)

designed to restore biological continuums by bridging over communication routes.

In Switzerland, all existing wildlife corridors of national importance were catalogued in 2001. Of the 303 recognised corridors of supra-regional importance, 47 have been classified as unusable and over half (171) now only partially fulfil their function. Only 85 (about one third) are intact. This study shows, as associations and certain authorities have already pointed out, that new measures are necessary to restore ecology networks for wildlife. The aims of this approach were set out in a Directive of the competent Ministry (DETEC) in 2001, laying down dimensions for large fauna pathways. A standard high-level crossing point, allowing large fauna moving along a corridor of supra-regional importance to cross a motorway, must have a useable width for fauna of 45 (+/- 5) metres. A reduced high-level crossing point of 25 (+/- 5) metres is adequate for a narrow road or in cases where the structure is intended for one species in particular. Finally, a small crossing

point may measure from 20-30 centimetres (passages for amphibians) to 30 or 40 metres (for ungulates for example). The other strong point of this Directive is the concept of adapting motorways for large fauna. This concept provides for the building of 51 crossing points in the coming decades, twenty or so of them by 2013. There are currently 24 such structures in Switzerland.

FRAGMENTATION OF AQUATIC HABITATS

Such linear transport infrastructures as canals and dams have different kinds of impact on the fragmentation of aquatic habitats. This type of infrastructure creates discontinuity within river corridors and between the different aquatic environments. It can also cause the disappearance or modification of aquatic environments owing to the general impact of the structure or its influence on the local hydrological systems. The particular feature of the relationship between natural aquatic habitat fragmentation and transport infrastructures is that watercourses and rivers can act as barriers for some species while at the same time providing corridors for other more aquatic species.

Major migratory fish species such as the salmon *(Salmo salar)* and the Allis shad *(Alosa alosa)* are born in a river and then swim out to sea to grow, returning to the same river to reproduce. Others, such as the eel *(Anguilla anguilla)*, are born in the sea and swim up rivers to grow.

Salmon swimming upstream

In all cases migration is a vital phase in these species' biological cycles, and dams and locks are major obstacles to migratory fish on their way upriver. Installing mechanisms to allow fish through, commonly known as fish channels, reduces or offsets the problems of such obstacles to migration. The efficiency of bypass mechanisms will however depend on density of obstacles and their physical characteristics.

Fish channels have a long history as biological corridors. The earliest fish channels date back to the 19th century, when they were designed to preserve fish as an economic resource. Ideally, fish channels should be converted into small bypass streams in order to reproduce natural conditions. However, where space is lacking, more technical amenities such as fish ladders or fish lifts can be installed.

Marsh near the Dnepr (UKR)

17 Open spaces along navigable watercourses

Maintaining open spaces along navigable watercourses is geared not only to facilitating floodwater runoff but also to maintaining a living space for fauna and flora. Preserving the freedom of riverbed displacement also facilitates maintenance of the erosion and sediment transport and deposit processes which make up fluvial dynamics. If the measures taken to promote the preservation of open areas for rivers are mainly motivated by flooding and flood damage, they do help restore and often protect major biological corridors.

Swiss legislation has taken account of the importance of preserving open spaces along watercourses. Article 21 of the Watercourse Development Order stipulates that the cantons must determine the minimum space needed for watercourses in order to prevent flooding and preserve ecological functions. This provision further specifies that the cantons must take account of the spatial needs of watercourses in their master plans and land-use plans, as well as in other activities affecting land organisation.

The World Conservation Congress Resolution 2.47: 'Conservation of the last wild rivers of Europe' has called on European States to conserve the last European wild rivers, such as Belaya,

Danube delta, Desna, Dnepr, Loire, Northern Dwina & Youg, Oka, Pechora, Pripjet, Sava, Tisza, Udaj, Ural, Viatka, Vistula, Volga delta, Vychegda, West Dwina – Daugava, and a number of smaller rivers, to preserve all remaining wild and semi-wild rivers in a close-to- natural state, to stop some river canalisation and damming programmes, to prepare independent strategic environmental impact assessments of the economic and ecological consequences of river regulation projects, and to initiate programmes to 're-naturalise' some river sections, aiming to prevent the loss of the biological elements native to particular catchment areas.

The Loire, for example, is one European river which has retained its freedom of riverbed displacement over extensive sections of its course. The Loire presents a remarkable continuum of ecologically rich natural and semi-natural areas. It is a genuine biological corridor, and has been the subject of a national restoration and conservation plan entitled Programme Loire Grandeur Nature. This programme has received 'Life' funding from the European Union, enabling it to purchase land to preserve the open spaces along the Loire, i.e. the recovery of natural flooding and displacement areas.

The Loire (F)

18

Management of roadsides in the Walloon Region (Belgium)

The Walloon Region has developed a particularly interesting roadside protection policy prohibiting the use of herbicides on verges, embankments and other public areas included in or adjacent to road infrastructures, including motorways, in watercourses, ponds and lakes and along their banks, in the case of publicly-owned roads. The Region can also conclude 'Roadside' contracts with the municipalities, whereby the latter undertake to draw up management plans in order to rationalise late mowing of roadside grass areas, subject to certain criteria. The Region provides the commune (municipality) with explanatory signposts and technical support in devising 'mowing plans' that differentiate between intensive and extensive mowing areas and looks after the organisation in space and time of the

mowing programmes. The late mowing method is implemented outside the intensively mowed sensitive areas. For instance, a 1 m strip adjacent to the road can be mown as often as necessary, while the rest of the verge is not mown until after 1 August. The success of this project as run by the Walloon Ministry shows the efficiency of certain non-binding measures. Furthermore, the use of specific standard signposting throughout the territory heightens public awareness of the importance of roadsides for biodiversity.

Maintenance contracts are being developed in this field for both roadsides and watercourse banks. Based on voluntary work, usually provided by municipalities, they are generally highly successful. The nature conservation interests at stake are thus backed up by a certain aesthetic input.

USING LINEAR INFRASTRUCTURES
TO ESTABLISH CORRIDORS

Paradoxically, road and rail transport infrastructures can sometimes play a positive role in wild fauna and flora migration. While a new infrastructure has negative effects on the environment, proper management of the impact of road, rail and river traffic can help promote certain aspects of biodiversity. Verges, central reservations, embankments and ditches are important areas that can accommodate wild fauna and flora, providing that ecological methods are used to maintain them. Ecological maintenance precludes, for instance, herbicides and extensive mowing late in the season.

Green areas adjacent to motorways and railway embankments require a very specific mode of management. The green areas in question along motorways are strips of vegetation located on either side of the actual motorway surface between the hard shoulder and the fencing, which means that they are an integral part of the motorway network. Since 1978, the company, Autoroutes du Sud de la France, which manages the parts of the motorway network assigned to it by the State, has been developing a policy of extensive management of motorway green areas. Under this policy, a guide to the mainte-

nance of green areas was drawn up in 1992. The Maintenance Charter set out in this guide lays down various rules on extensive management of the areas. For instance, the planting techniques and maintenance methods used must involve a huge reduction in chemical weed clearance. The guide also stipulates that scrub clearance should never be conducted in spring, which is the breeding season for many animal species.

Co-operation as a basis for the international implementation of the Pan-European Ecological Network

Operational ecological networks at a transboundary, national or regional/local level will be a main contribution to the establishment of PEEN. As indicated in the introduction to this chapter, operational ecological networks will ensure the functionality of both PEEN core areas, where these have not yet been protected under international designations, and PEEN corridors (Council of Europe, 2000).

Although an increasing number of potential ecological networks have been designed, and although many have gained legal or political endorsement at national or sub-national level, as shown in Chapter 2, not many of these networks can as yet be considered fully operational because it cannot be guaranteed that they will function properly. As in the Netherlands and Switzerland, work on establishing corridors has begun on the ground. Talks are also ongoing between Switzerland and Germany to establish transboundary corridors. While the initial results of these different approaches have been positive, it is difficult to assess to what extent these networks contribute to connectivity at Pan-European level and, thereby, to PEEN.

However, the development of a coherent spatial structure for nature conservation in Europe, transcending administrative boundaries which have no real ecological basis, calls for synergetic action. Such synergy involves co-operation, both between protected areas and between States and even local authorities. Like the global Parks for Peace initiative developed by IUCN, international co-operation in connection with the Pan-European Ecological Network serves both as a basis for sustainable protection of nature areas and as a means of fostering constructive political relationships between countries.

National and regional co-operation

International co-operation on nature conservation is gradually developing, both within countries and between States. Map 3 (Chapter 1) shows that many European countries have already developed or are in the process of developing a national or sub-national ecological network. In nearly all cases this network is in the planning phase, with implementation on the ground a long and difficult process. This requires the involvement of many stakeholders. At least 16 European countries have legislation that incorporates the concept of ecological networks. Map 3 also shows that transboundary co-operation is necessary in order to ensure that ecological networks continue across borders and are not disrupted by administrative boundaries.

The progress made so far opens the way to co-ordinated management of transboundary areas. Such co-operation is needed to restore ecological continuity in specific areas, and examples show how important it is for all natural areas, whether protected or not.

Transboundary co-operation between protected areas

The inclusion of a transboundary protected area in an international network of sites encourages institutional contacts between managers of areas on either side of the border, as well as providing a legal and political context for co-operation (Brunner, 2002).

Tarpan horse : Extinct wild forests' species in the late XIXth century, the Tarpan horse was reintroduced thanks to a special plan carried out by the Bialowieza National Park's reserve (PL). Consequently, a wild horde has been living again in the north forests. (Source : www. park.bialowieza.com).

19

Bialowieza Forest: an example of co-operation between transboundary protected areas

Located on the watershed between the Baltic Sea and the Black Sea, this vast forest complex retains a primeval ecological structure, making it one of the last remaining fragments of natural plain forest in Europe. It contains outstanding fauna, including rare mammals such as wolf, lynx and otter, as well as some 300 European bison, a species reintroduced to the site.

Shared by Poland and Belarus, the Bialowieza Forest was protected by national legislation on either side of the border. In 1979, the Polish part was recognized as a World Heritage site. In 1992, Unesco extended World Heritage status to the strictly protected adjacent section: the Belovezhskaya Pushcha national park in Belarus. In 1996, the Belarus Belovezhskaya Pushcha national park and the Polish Bialowieza national park were jointly awarded the European Diploma. A pilot project for an ecological network, co-ordinated by ECNC Natuurmo-numenten, as well as the directors of the protected areas in this area, was finalised in 2005.

*Transboundary protected areas
recognized by international designation*

The objectives of the Unesco World Cultural and Natural Heritage Convention include international co-operation on site management. A number of transboundary sites have been added to the World Heritage List in recent years, providing scope for greater pooling of knowledge and management techniques.

A single European Diploma was first awarded to a transboundary protected area – the Germano-Luxembourg Nature Park – in 1973. The new regulation adopted by the Committee of Ministers of the Council of Europe in 1998, which lays down conditions and criteria for awarding the diploma, provides that *"in the case of transboundary areas, a sole Diploma shall not be granted without the consent of all the States concerned. "*

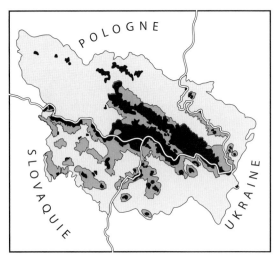

Map 13 : Transboundary Biosphere Reserve between Poland, Ukraine and Slovakia. Source: Unesco

Numerous transboundary areas in Europe have been awarded the Council of Europe's Diploma of protected areas. Through this award, these zones try to implement a co-ordinated management system. Examples : the National Park of Mercantour (France) and the Natural Park of Maritime Alps (Italy), The National Park of Thayatal (Austria) and The National Park of Podyji (Czech Republic).

These international designations, which are very similar to a seal of quality (label), do not impose any specific obligations on States. They do, however, enable managers of protected areas to maintain special relationships as part of an organised framework facilitating the development of common projects. Other international organisations also recognize

transboundary sites, with the stated aims of co-ordination and management.

One of the primary objectives of the Seville Strategy for Biosphere Reserves (1995), intended to consolidate the world network of Biosphere Reserves, is to 'promote and facilitate twinning between biosphere reserve sites and foster transboundary reserves'. Co-ordinating the management of transboundary biosphere reserves has become a priority for the Man and Biosphere programme. Recommendations for the Establishment and Functioning of Transboundary Biosphere Reserves were recently adopted. Establishing transboundary biosphere reserves does not necessarily involve developing a joint structure or common procedures. Rather, the purpose of such recognition is to co-ordinate activities and to ensure that the work of both organizations is consistent and contributes to a shared heritage. A co-operation framework must be established for the implementation of practical activities. Under the new zoning scheme for Biosphere Reserves applicable to transboundary areas, a number of dispersed core areas may be brought together within a territory subject to management rules compatible with the maintenance of a certain degree of biological diversity; this is an initial step towards the establishment of transboundary linking zones between nature areas and, therefore, of transboundary ecological networks.

Alpine Network of Protected Areas

The subject of transboundary protected areas and the establishment of spatial links between protected Alpine areas is central to the Alpine Convention. The Contracting Parties to the Alpine Convention have emphasised that only large Alpine protected areas forming a coherent ecological unit could ensure sustainable protection of the Alpine landscape and the continuity of natural processes. They instructed the Alpine Network of Protected Areas to analyse the existing potential of protected areas and transboundary links and to suggest practical measures. The Alpine Region includes several transboundary protected areas as well as large protected areas covering more than 1000 ha; this makes it possible to envisage ecological continuity between sites stretching from the Franco-Italian border to Austria's eastern border.

In eight pilot zones, a number of areas have been analysed using selected indicators, and recognized as having significant ecological potential as ecological corridors or linking zones. This study shows that numerous protected areas are linked to harmonised. Emphasis was also placed on the important contribution made to the development of a coherent ecological space by policies in sectors such as agriculture, transport and spatial planning.

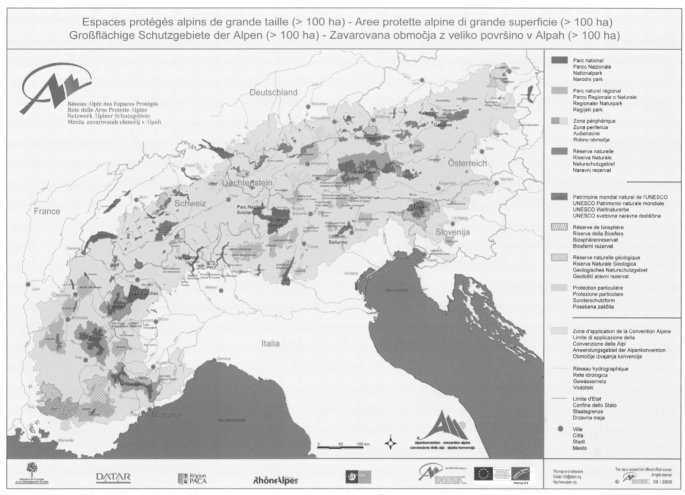

Espaces protégés alpins de grande taille (> 100 ha) - Aree protette alpine di grande superficie (> 100 ha)
Großflächige Schutzgebiete der Alpen (> 100 ha) - Zavarovana območja z veliko površino v Alpah (> 100 ha)

Map 14 : Map of the Alpine Network of Large Protected Areas. Source: Alpine Convention, 2005.

one another across national borders or within the same country. There are an estimated 250 km of common international borders between different categories of protected areas, and co-operation between these areas could act as a driving force for the establishment of biological links.

Une étude réalisée dans la zone du Parc national The study conducted in the zone comprising the Mercantour National Park (France), the Alpi Marittime Nature Park and the Alta Valle Pesio e Tanaro Nature Park (Italy) shows that this region, which is very remote, does actually serve as a biological corridor. This was confirmed by monitoring a number of marked ibex, which left the Mercantour National Park and travelled south-west to the Haute Provence geological reserve. The study also identified specific objectives for the development of an Alpine ecological network. In particular, objectives and measures relating to protected areas should be

Golden eagle

The Alpine Network is also involved in co-operation arrangements outside the Alps. A network of protected areas in the Carpathian mountains is at the planning stage, as is a similar initiative in the Pyrenees and the Cantabrian mountains. Since these mountain ranges form a macroscopic ecological continuum, partnership projects are envisaged within the 'Cantabrian-Pyrenees-Alps Great Mountain Corridor: Rebuilding natural bridges across Europe' project'.

Marmots, Queyras (F)

The Lower Danube green corridor

Dalmatian Pelicans, Danube Delta

In June 2000, Romania, Bulgaria, Ukraine and Moldova signed an agreement on the conservation of flood areas and wetlands in the Danube and Black Sea Basin and the creation of a protected area in the region around the river's delta. The Environment Ministers of the four countries signed an initial agreement in Bucharest, providing for the establishment of a green corridor in the Lower Danube Basin, designed to extend existing protected areas – covering 773,166 hectares – by some 300,000 hectares.

This corridor will include wetlands, lakes, alluvial forests and water-meadows. More than 80% of the Danube Basin's wetlands

and flood-zones were destroyed during the last century. The agreement will also help to create jobs in the fishing and tourism sectors and prevent and reduce pollution in the lower Danube basin.

Inter-state co-operation

Co-operation between Pan-European states can take various forms. Although this involves very challenging processes, Europe features a growing number of examples of co-operation aimed at establishing connectivity between natural areas.

Econet for Central Asia

Central Asia is a region of 4 million km2, uniting five independent countries. On their own initiative the countries of the region perform as a united body in a lot of initiatives on environmental conservation and sustainable development through the Interregional Sustainable Development Commission and development of the Regional Environmental Action Plan (REAP). Using this opportunity, WWF in co-operation with various stakeholders of the region, is developing a project for an ecological network for the whole region. The main goal of the project is the creation of a united ecological network of the region of Central Asia and its integration in the regional and national sustainable development plans.

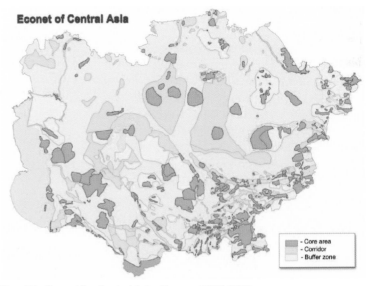

Map 15 : Econet for Central Asia. Source: WWF, 2006.

In 2006, this Econet project was adopted by the States of the Central Asian region as the framework for development of national protected area plans.

The Caucasus Ecoregion

A project for an ecological network in the Caucasus region has been developed, identifying Priority Conservation Areas (PCA), as well as potential corridors. PCAs and Corridors are to be the foundation for the development of an ecological network in the Caucasus ecoregion. This network will be based on existing and future protected areas as well as the sustainable use of natural resources through adequate land management methods – as described in the Ecoregional Conservation Plan for the Caucasus (WWF Caucasus Programme, 2006)

Curtain) or current (e.g. the external border of the EU), need to be overcome when working with nature.

Although developed from a political as opposed to an ecological background, the Green Belt travels down parts of the Eastern Flyway for bird species, crosses several large mammal migration routes and covers 8 of Europe's 11 biogeographical zones. It also touches on some of Europe's major protected areas. This project, supported inter alia by the IUCN, is divided into three areas: the Fennoscandian green belt, which runs between Norway, Finland and the Russian Federation; the Central European green belt, which crosses Germany, the Czech Republic,

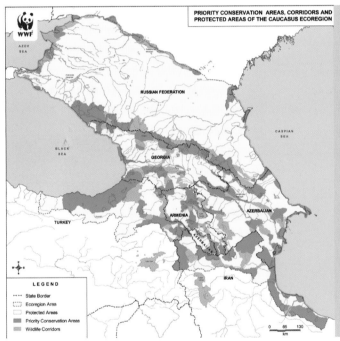

Priority Conservation Areas (PCA)

indicate areas most important for biodiversity conservation at an ecoregional level. The areas outside these priority areas are also important – for specific groups of animals, for certain plants and ecosystems, or as corridors. But priority conservation areas are important for the largest number of animals, plants and ecosystems (as far as they are known today). Corridors indicate areas important for migration and dispersal of large mammals, birds and fish, especially between Priority Conservation Areas.

Map 16: Project of ecological network in Caucasus - Map of Priority Conservation Areas (PCA) and Corridors in the Caucasus ecoregion, © WWF Caucasus Programme, 2006.

The Green Belt

The Iron Curtain was a political barrier separating the countries of Europe for 40 years. The area around the barrier was a forbidden zone to human activity and so nature was allowed to prosper. The European Green Belt aims to use the memory of this barrier to create the backbone of an ecological network running the full length of Europe from the Barents Sea to the Adriatic and Black Seas. The initiative aims to support transboundary co-operation for nature conservation and sustainable development within rural areas. The Green Belt serves as a reminder that barriers, be they historical (e.g. the Iron

Slovakia and Hungary; and the Balkans green belt, which ends at the Black Sea.

The Rhine 2020 programme

During the 13th Ministerial Conference on the Rhine, Ministers of the five Rhine Riparian Statesand European Community representatives adopted a programme on the sustainable development of the river over the next twenty years. The primary aim of 'Rhine 2020' is to restore the Rhine's ecological functions while guaranteeing its use as a major navigation route. The programme will be co-ordinated with the new European Water Outline Directive.

The 'Rhine 2020' programme specifies the sequence of measures to be taken. The first priority is to reactivate large swathes of the former inundation areas and to protect valuable ecosystems. The programme combines ecological interests with flood prevention and the protection of surface and underground water in the Rhine area. This sustainable development plan embraces ecological, economic and social aspects simultaneously.

Wadden Sea: an example of trilateral co-operation

The Wadden Sea is a coastal sea extending 450 kilometres along the North Sea coasts of the Netherlands, Germany and Denmark. A network of tidal channels, sands, mud flats, salt marshes and islands forms a transition area between land and sea that experiences

Map 17: Extension of the Green Belt project. Source: IUCN Europe, 2006

daily tidal changes and considerable variations in salinity, light, oxygen levels and temperature. The result is a complex ecosystem affording an exceptional habitat for very diverse fauna and flora. Trilateral co-operation (the Netherlands, Germany and Denmark) for the protection of the Wadden Sea was established in 1982. A joint structure was set up to manage co-operation in this transboundary maritime area. The legal basis for co-operation was gradually formalised, changing from a political declaration in 1982 to a formal agreement in 1987, with a view to managing the Wadden Sea as a single ecological unit. As part of this formalised co-operation, the Common Wadden Sea Secretariat, based in Germany, was set up to guide and co-ordinate the trilateral strategy and conservation and management activities in the area.

Seal (Wadden Sea, NL)

Local co-operation on the setting-up of ecological networks

Transboundary co-operation between local authorities, which is necessary for the effective maintenance of biological diversity, emerged only at a late stage. The main reason is that, traditionally, only the State could engage in international relations. Local authorities can now co-operate with their transboundary counterparts in the field of nature conservation, and a number of transboundary ecological networks are in the process of being set up. Co-operative mechanisms within specific areas can also be used to set up ecological networks at local level.

Transboundary co-operation

The Regiobogen project

The 'Regiobogen: a Tri-national Green Belt in the 3-Border Region' project is of particular interest owing to its trinational focus. This project aims to develop a biotope grid system in the 'three-border' region between France, Germany and Switzerland. It will also provide an opportunity to bring together all the significant nature conservation data supplied by public authorities, universities and associations in the three countries within a geographical information system (GIS). The achievement of ecological objectives is divided into a number of stages. The first stage involved recording environmental data and presenting them in graphic form, thereby making it possible to monitor natural areas, identify conflicts and plan nature conservation measures. The aim of the next stage will be to co-ordinate nature and landscape conservation projects and other projects such as traffic or urban growth plans, with a view to connecting core areas

Fish channel (2000) (D)

in the region by means of linking zones. The programme uses various mechanisms to connect the most interesting biotopes, for instance by encouraging more extensive use of agricultural areas, revitalisation of rivers and restoration of wetlands.

The Walloon-Luxembourg and Netherlands basic transboundary ecological and landscape plan

The basic transboundary ecological plan is a tripartite government initiative between Belgium, Luxembourg and the Netherlands, implemented by local authorities, co-financed with Interreg funding. It stems from a desire on the part of these governments to apply the concepts developed in the Pan-European Biological and Landscape Diversity Strategy to this transbound-

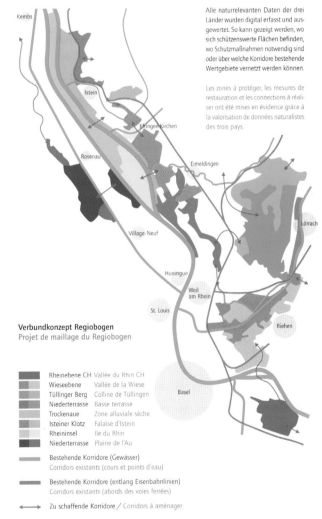

ary area. The aim of the basic transboundary ecological plan is to develop a joint approach to transboundary environmental issues in Belgium, Luxembourg and the Netherlands. It should provide scope for generating practical projects with a view to strengthening environmental relationships between the three partners.

Map 18: Map of the Regiobogen project. Source: www.truz.org/regiobogen/, 2006

On this basis, two drafts are being prepared simultaneously, one involving the Flemish Region and the Netherlands, and the other involving the Walloon Region and Luxembourg.

The draft basic transboundary ecological and landscape plan involving the Walloon Region and Luxembourg aims to promote integrated regional development in border areas. The plan will eventually apply to all municipalities along the border between the Luxembourg and the Walloon Region. Phase II of the plan, which is currently in progress, consists in identifying ecological networks in 14 municipalities. The networks thus identified are made up of core areas earmarked primarily for nature conservation, development areas where nature conservation is compatible with other ways of using the environment, and linking zones, which are generally linear areas that support movement by wild flora and fauna species and connect core areas with development zones. These linking zones may be made up of hedges and lines of trees, rocky and grassy banks or watercourses. A fact-sheet is drawn up for each area included in the ecological network, and incorporated into a common database of sites of ecological interest, designed to allow comparisons between, and optimisation of, existing data with a view to conserving a comprehensive range of ecosystems, species, habitats and landscapes.

Map 19: : Geographical scope of the basic transboundary ecological and landscape plan for the Walloon and Luxembourg part. Source: Ministry of Walloon Region, 2006.

Intra-national co-operation

The development of ecological networks is aimed primarily at conserving and restoring core areas, buffer zones and biological interconnections. The main purpose of corridors is to re-establish links between different areas of the ecological network. The development of ecological networks also has impacts at ecological, cultural, aesthetic and even sociological levels. As well as restoring links between areas of unspoilt land, the re-introduction of natural zones around built-up areas has the effect of re-establishing links between human beings and nature, and between city-dwellers and rural areas (Mougenot & Roussel, 2002). The restoration of ecological interconnections also benefits rural areas, particularly for combating soil erosion and flooding.

The protection of corridors may also entail social behaviour compatible with sustainable development. This applies, for example, to church administrators who agree to protect steeples in order to encourage bats, farmers who agree to delay their harvests in order to allow young Montagu's Harriers *(Circus pygargus)* to take flight, and motorists who agree to modify their route in the light of the spring migration of frogs and toads. The development of ecological networks leads to greater involvement of various players associated with spatial planning. Associations are increasingly being acknowledged as partners of the administrative departments responsible for spatial planning. Similarly, local authorities and even private bodies can take action to protect the environment through the maintenance or restoration of natural areas or biological interconnections.

Ecological networks must be implemented in practice; local and regional authorities are responsible for their management (Council of Europe, 2001/2). Thanks to their planning, investment, regulatory, management and enforcement powers, local and regional authorities can take action to address local issues. A number of regulatory instruments are available to local authorities for the development of eco-

Montagu's harrier

The project was based on the principle that municipalities should volunteer. The procedure

20 A path to ecological connectivity around Vitoria-Gasteiz (Basque country, Spain)

The Green Belt of Vitoria-Gasteiz is the result of an ambitious environmental restoration and recovery plan for the outlying districts of the city. The basic aim of the plan is to recover the ecological and social value of this space through the creation of a natural continuum around the city built around a number of different environments of high ecological and landscape value. The Green Belt project around Vitoria-Gasteiz is to protect a circular mountain route that runs through the main pastoral landscapes of the Basque Country and links up spaces on the Natura 2000 Network and other landscapes of special beauty. It provides:
• a chance to connect nature to nature by connecting more than 100,000 ha of

Natura 2000 areas around the town and at the same time solving the fragmentation of existing environmental hot spots;
• a chance to connect people to nature through a network of over 700 km of footpaths, that takes city- dwellers to the countryside and brings the countryside to the city-dwellers;
• a chance to connect nature to culture sustaining the age-old way of life of more than 200 shepherds.
In October 2006 the authorities of the Basque Province of Alava and of the town of Vitoria-Gasteiz published a declaration on their activities to stimulate the ecological connectivity between the Cantabrian Mountains and the Pyrenees.

logical networks. New instruments can also be tried, as the experience of the Walloon Region shows.

The Belgian municipal nature development plans

Municipal nature development plans are the result of an initiative by the King Baudouin Foundation (Biodiversity Contracts). As part of European Nature Conservation Year in 1995, the Walloon Region followed the King Baudouin Foundation's example by extending and adapting the project to a larger number of municipalities through the introduction of municipal nature development plans. Municipal nature development plans serve the same purpose as the previous biodiversity contracts, but biodiversity is developed from a new standpoint: the 'ecological network'.

for implementing municipal nature development plans is laid down by the Walloon Region. The plans cover a five-year period, and receive financial assistance from the Walloon Region.

These plans are not confined to the field of nature conservation, but also include other action taken by municipalities in the area of sustainable development (Stein & Wolf, 1995). With respect to establishing biological corridors, natural and landscape heritage inventories are an essential component of the plan, and confer scientific value on it. The approval of the plan by municipal authorities gives it political, if not legal force. An inventory of municipal natural and landscape heritage must then be compiled. Generally carried out by consultants, such inventories make it possible to map the various biotopes forming the ecological network. The plans, finalised within a large partnership with the stakeholders concerned, have been a genuine success with Belgian municipal authorities.

Need for inter-municipal co-operation with a view to protecting ecological networks

The inter-municipal level is essential if the spatial development of ecological networks is to take account of measures implemented in adjoining areas. By combining the concept

features. They do not have direct legal effect, but are a tool that can assist in the decision-making process.

Green plans take into account local features arising from a landscape's topography, geology, pedology, hydrography, climate, fauna and flora and biotopes (and the links between them), as well as its cultural and historical value. The Association, wishing to achieve the natural resource protection objectives set out in the 'green plan', incorporated the protection and restoration

Opération
Combles et Clochers

MINISTERE DE LA REGION WALLONNE
Division de la Nature et des Forêts
Av. Prince de Liège, 7 - 5100 JAMBES
Tél : 0800 - 1 1901
Http://mrw.wallonie.be/dgrne/dnf/comblesetclochers

Lofts and steeples operation

Numerous animal species are found in the lofts, attics and steeples of buildings. Accordingly, the Walloon Region launched the Lofts and Steeples operation in 1995. Since then, the Ministry of the Walloon Region and participating municipalities have been working together to protect certain species (bat, barn owl, jackdaw and common swift). The Ministry of the Walloon Region grants subsidies to participating municipalities for the necessary conservation work. This project is based on a voluntary agreement between the municipalities and the Walloon Region.
Source: Ministry of the Walloon Region, 2006.

of inter-municipal co-operation with that of ecological networks, it is possible to achieve sustainable regional development, providing scope both for co-operation between the various players involved and for the incorporation of nature and landscape conservation into development policies.

SICONA (Luxembourg)

In 1989, 10 municipalities in the Kehlen region (Luxembourg) joined together to form an Inter-municipal Nature Conservation Association (SICONA). The aim was to enhance green areas and to implement green plans dating back to the early 1980s. Green plans are planning instruments designed to ensure the protection and management of the environment and natural resources in non-urbanised areas. They contain proposals for ecological management of the landscape on the basis of a scientific assessment of its key

of ecological interconnections into its activities. It undertakes numerous activities in the field of nature conservation. To focus solely on those with a direct bearing on the development of biological corridors, examples include hedge height and the leasing of a five-metre strip from farmers in order to plant trees.

The Association is financed by municipalities. Each municipality finances the activities undertaken by the Association within its boundaries, and makes an annual contribution to its operation. This Inter-municipal Association, which was initially fairly small, now has 19 member municipalities. A biological station has also been set up to undertake scientific monitoring, and to initiate and carry out species conservation projects. The success of this system is also demonstrated by the fact that other inter-municipal nature conservation associations have been set up in Luxembourg.

Master Plan
for the Grenoble region (France)

The semi-public association *(syndicat mixte)* for the Grenoble region has used a comprehensive zoning and development plan to incorporate the protection of biological corridors into its spatial planning. Comprehensive spatial and development plans, initially designed to organise the development of conurbations, have gradually incorporated environmental concerns, and now focus on setting *"basic spatial planning guidelines for the areas in question, bearing in mind the need to strike a balance between urban growth, the pursuit of agricultural activities and other economic activities, the preservation of air quality and the conservation of habitats and natural and urban sites and landscapes."*

Inter alia, the plan for the Grenoble region states that, *"in order to support biodiversity, links must be re-established between habitats fragmented by urbanisation and major infrastructure by means of natural corridors. In addition, the hydrographical network must be restored in terms of both its irrigation functions and the connections it provides between different habitats."* Accordingly, along the hydrographical network and surrounding wetlands, a minimum 10-metre strip of land on either side of the watercourse must be classified as a natural area. This binding provision also applies to the edges of new urban areas and to new roads. The purpose of this measure is to preserve an untilled strip of land, and to allow suitable vegetation to grow there. The plan provides that the necessary development work may be undertaken, while stating that *"such corridors must be subject to stringent preservation and enhancement measures."*

At Département level, the Isère General Council has commissioned a study of the ecological network within the Département. This study is used to explain the concept of ecological networks to the general public and to administrative departments.

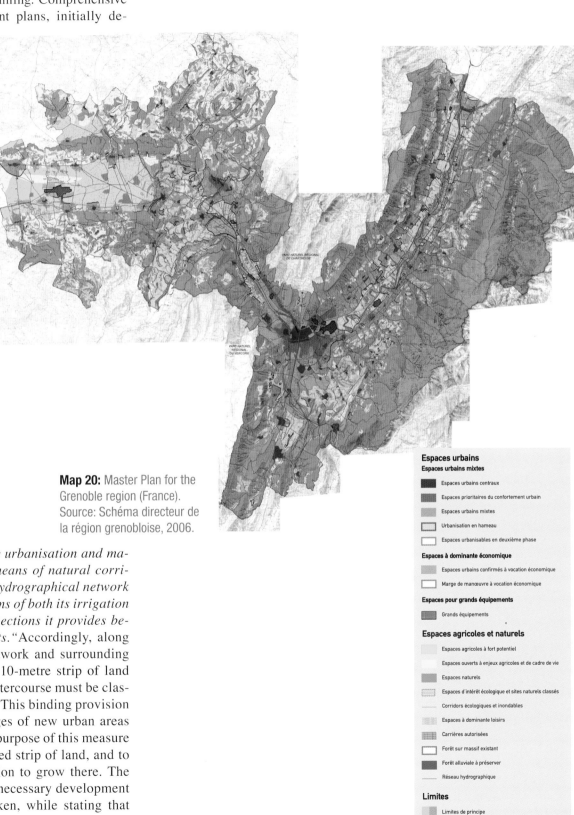

Map 20: Master Plan for the Grenoble region (France). Source: Schéma directeur de la région grenobloise, 2006.

Espaces urbains
Espaces urbains mixtes
- Espaces urbains centraux
- Espaces prioritaires du confortement urbain
- Espaces urbains mixtes
- Urbanisation en hameau
- Espaces urbanisables en deuxième phase

Espaces à dominante économique
- Espaces urbains confirmés à vocation économique
- Marge de manœuvre à vocation économique

Espaces pour grands équipements
- Grands équipements

Espaces agricoles et naturels
- Espaces agricoles à fort potentiel
- Espaces ouverts à enjeux agricoles et de cadre de vie
- Espaces naturels
- Espaces d'intérêt écologique et sites naturels classés
- Corridors écologiques et inondables
- Espaces à dominante loisirs
- Carrières autorisées
- Forêt sur massif existant
- Forêt alluviale à préserver
- Réseau hydrographique

Limites
- Limites de principe
- Limites stratégiques

Alpine landscape (I)

The local level is crucial for acceptance of the practical implementation of ecological networks, and for day-to-day consideration of nature. Public involvement is therefore particularly important for the development of ecological networks. It is at local and regional level that the public can directly express itself, and it may be helpful to try and involve private landowners and economic players at the earliest possible stage. Their specific constraints and objectives can thereby be taken into account from the outset, making for lasting projects.

Implementation of local 'Agenda 21' provides an opportunity to combine biodiversity conservation through ecological networks and sustainable development of territories through extensive involvement of local stakeholders, in a long-term perspective.

22

Implementation of municipal nature development plans in Ukraine

The introduction of municipal nature development plans in eight municipalities situated in the Nemiriv district in Ukraine is an example of the practical implementation of ecological networks at local level. This project is the result of a co-operation agreement between the Walloon Region (Belgium), Ukraine and the Council of Europe.

During the initial phase of the agreement, draft municipal nature development plans were drawn up for each municipality involved in the pilot project. The second phase served to identify important areas for biodiversity conservation, to organize the management of these areas with a view to sustainable development and to put in place a campaign designed to explain the concept of ecological networks to the local population. In early 2005, the project participants launched nine mini-projects aimed at developing ecological networks.

These projects are numerous and very varied. They range from the enhancement of nature areas to the organisation of grazing in sensitive natural habitats and the development of eco-tourism. What the different projects have in common is the involvement of schools and awareness-raising among pupils. This active involvement of young people holds out the prospect of greater public awareness of the natural heritage in the years to come.

The Pan-European Ecological Network funding instruments

Various bodies – private and public – fund projects contributing to the development of the Pan-European Ecological Network. Through Community financing programmes, the European Union promotes both co-operation in member states and nature conservation within and outside the Union. In addition, some countries which have implemented and tested ecological network concepts within their boundaries provide financial assistance for the development of such networks in other countries.

23

The Global Environment Facility

was set up in 1991 to promote co-operation and finance projects in four focal areas in which the planet's environment was seriously threatened: diminishing biodiversity, climate change, deterioration of international waters and thinning of the ozone layer. The GEF than broadened the scope of its activities to land degradation, mainly through desertification and deforestation, and persistent organic pollutants.

In 2006 the GEF backed various projects forming part of a drive for greater connectivity between natural areas, including the project on Conservation and Sustainable Use of Biodiversity in the Kazakhstan sector of the Altai-Sayan Ecoregion.

Community funding

Specific instrument for the conservation of biological diversity

In order to promote and implement its Community environment policy, the European Union has set up the 'LIFE' financial instrument.

LIFE comprises three thematic strands. The objective of LIFE-Nature, one of these strands, is to contribute to the implementation of Community regulations on nature conservation. In order to be eligible, projects must contribute to the maintenance or restoration of natural habitats and/or species populations to a favourable conservation status within the meaning of the EC Habitats Directive.

Within the European Union, LIFE-Nature thereby supports the practical implementation of the Natura 2000 network by making possible numerous innovative trials in the field of biodiversity conservation. It also enables accession countries to work towards common biodiversity conservation objectives. The new LIFE+ programme (period 2007-2013) will chiefly support such initiatives as networking of best practices, communication and action to raise public awareness.

The following projects, which put particular emphasis on ecological networks and connectivity of natural and semi-natural habitats, have been financed by LIFE-Nature:

24

CRO-NEN Project (Croatia)

The CRO-NEN project was financed by the LIFE III programme in the 2002-2005 period. A map of Croatia's national ecological network was drawn up. Although Croatia is not yet a member of the European Union, the project afforded an opportunity to identify the country's potential Natura 2000 sites, serving as a basis for co-operation between the various public and private players involved in conservation.

Map 21: Map of the CRO-NEN project. Source: Croatia, State Institute for Nature Protection, 2005.

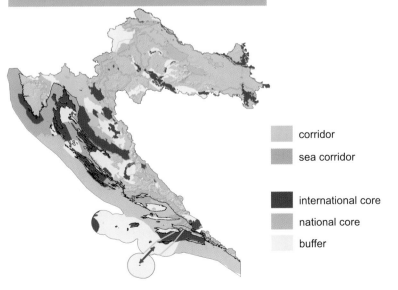

corridor

sea corridor

international core

national core

buffer

Title	Country (year)	Objectif
Functional ecological network in the Central Transylvanian Plain	Romania (2000)	Important Bird Area Restoration of 250 ha of wetlands, including ponds, marshes, swamps and fens, and afforestation of almost 450 ha with a view to re-establishing alluvial forests.
Building up the Croatian national ecological network as part of the Pan-European Ecological Network and Natura 2000	Croatia (2002)	The CRO-NEN project aims to: • identify areas that will be part of the Natura 2000 network when Croatia joins the EU; • develop the National Ecological Network and the Regional Ecological Network for Visegrad 4+2 countries; • facilitate exchanges between individuals.
Restoration of European otter habitats	Belgium (2005)	In order to ensure continuity with favourable otter (Lutra lutra) habitats in France and Germany, the project aims to restore otter habitats in a transboundary area between Belgium and the Grand Duchy of Luxembourg, including the basins of the Our, Sûre and Ourthe rivers, covering approximately 300,000 ha
Enhancing the protection of large carnivores in the Vrancea region	Romania (2005)	The aim of the project is to improve the conservation management of brown bear (Ursus arctos), Eurasian lynx (Lynx lynx) and grey wolf (Canis lupus) in the Vrancea region, which has the densest population of large carnivores in Romania. Inter alia, this is being done with a view to Romania's forthcoming entry to the European Union and thus the inclusion of this region in the Natura 2000 network.
Creation of ecological corridors for endangered species	Spain (1994)	The project covers the west of the Iberian Peninsula, which contains numerous endemic species. Most of the region's ecosystems are the result of traditional human activities that respect the environment, including the seasonal transfer of grazing animals. The action taken mainly involves the lease or purchase of pasture land and habitat restoration, including through reforestation, so as to maintain management activities compatible with the conservation of endangered species.

Table 2: Examples of projects related to ecological networks funded by LIFE Nature. EC-DG Environment

Other types of funding

The various types of Community funding which Member States use to co-finance management of the Natura 2000 sites are all relevant to the establishment of the Pan-European Ecological Network. They include the Cohesion Fund, the EAGGF (European Agricultural Guidance and Guarantee Fund) Guidance Section, and structural funds such as the ERDF (European Regional Development Fund), and the Interreg projects. The Regulation on Rural Development also opens the way to co-funding of rural development initiatives geared to implementation of Natura 2000, including the management of sites on farm and forest land. The European cohesion policy helps funding infrastructure connected with environmental projects and programmes in Natura 2000 sites, when these contribute to the region's general economic development. The positive social and economic effects of setting up ecological networks at local level are gradually being acknowledged, and this means that these funds can also be used to restore and protect biological corridors.

In 1990, the European Commission set up the Interreg programme to promote the development of transboundary and transnational regions. Although it was not primarily designed to combat fragmentation of natural areas, it is now used to promote links. In fact, the Interreg funding programmes, which initially focused on reducing customs barriers for socio-economic reasons, now pursue various aims, including protection of the environment and regional development. Projects aimed at defragmenting natural areas may thus be eligible for them. The Community initiative Interreg III (2000-2006), contributes to the development of interregional and transboundary co-operation by co-financing local projects. Three strands support different types of project: cross-border, transnational and interregional co-operation. Each of the three strands includes environmental protection among its objectives, and may be used to facilitate transboundary policies for the defragmentation of natural habitats. Several defragmentation projects have received Interreg funding.

25

Financing of a transnational ecological network project by Interreg

The Interreg North Sea Programme aims to develop transboundary co-operation in the field of spatial planning. It includes parts of Denmark, Germany, the Netherlands, Norway, Sweden and the United Kingdom. The programme's Priority no. 3 focuses on promotion of integrated management of coastal zones, protection of significant nature areas, management of natural resources and promotion of cultural tourism. A number of projects have been set up under Measure no. 3, which aims to restore ecological connectivity between natural areas.

Inter alia, the Transnational Ecological Network III project aims to restore the ecological functions of watercourses as part of a transboundary approach. The programme's main objective is to re-establish ecological corridors along canals and watercourses between Natura 2000 sites and other wildlife sites. An inter-disciplinary approach is encouraged, and projects must combine the revitalisation of watercourses for ecological purposes with measures that promote integrated ecosystem management fostering sustainable agriculture and, more generally, sustainable rural development. Four projects are under way in the Netherlands, the United Kingdom and Germany.

26

The European Biodiversity Resourcing Initiative (EBRI)

The European Biodiversity Resourcing Initiative (EBRI) was launched in the framework of the Pan-European Biological and Landscape Diversity Strategy (PEBLDS), following the request at the Fourth 'Environment for Europe' Ministerial Conference in Aarhus to the financial sector to increase its involvement in sustainable development issues. An operational framework was established in 2002 to bring the needs for biodiversity resourcing in Europe together with the interests of the Banking Community and International Financial Institutions (IFIs), with the ultimate aim of increasing the investments in bankable biodiversity activities in Europe. After that a European Task Force on Banking, Business and Biodiversity (ETF/BBB) was established

to ensure that information, expertise and project-related experience are available to potential entrepreneurs in Eastern Europe, Caucasus, and Central Asia (EECCA). The ETF/BBB consists of representatives of the European Bank for Reconstruction and Development, the Swiss Agency for Environment, Forests and Landscape, the Ministry of Environment and Water of Hungary, the Ministry of Agriculture, Nature and Food Quality of the Netherlands, Rabobank Nederland, the Department for Environment, Food and Rural Affairs of the United Kingdom and the United Nations Environment Programme Regional Office for Europe. The work on banking and biodiversity could assist in mobilizing pro-biodiversity investments in PEEN core areas or corridors.

State participation in funding of the Pan-European Ecological Network

In addition to the incentive mechanism which exists at international and Community level, States help to fund the ecological networks. They have structures for co-operation and the pooling of experience, but individual States can also use tax incentives to promote the restoration of biological interconnections.

Since 1993, Swiss agricultural policy has offered financial incentives to develop Ecological Compensation Areas (known as SCEs). There are 16 types of SCE, such

Channels dug into the rock centuries ago have been irrigating mountain agriculture with water from melted glaciers, particularly in Wallis, Switzerland.

as extensive and less intensive grasslands, extensive pastures, litter meadows, hedges or standard fruit trees. It is compulsory within the framework of Cross-Compliance for Swiss farmers to manage at least 7% of their agriculturally useful land areas (SAUs) as SCEs, if they wish to benefit from direct payments. Approximately 10% of all Switzerland's SAUs are currently managed as SCEs. In order to promote networking of these areas and to improve their biological quality, the Ecological Quality Order (OQE, 2001) provides for results-based incentives. It has subsequently been mainly in mountain and hill regions that numerous SCEs have been networked, in the framework of the National Ecology Network (REN). It is planned to increase financial incentives for networking in 2008, so as to overcome the deficit currently observed in the plains.

The Netherlands nature management plan for Central and Eastern European countries

The Netherlands instigated the debate on biological corridors in Europe, particularly within the Union, by proposing that a connectivity objective be included in the EC Habitats Directive and inviting the States to develop an EECONET (European Ecological Network). Within its national co-operation programmes the Netherlands provides considerable assistance to countries wishing to develop nature conservation policies

27

The Caucasus Protected Areas Fund

WWF, Conservation International, the German Ministry for Economic Development and Co-operation, and the German International Development Bank are together setting up a fund to provide long-term financial support for protected areas in Georgia, Azerbaijan and Armenia.

The fund will finance projects of major biological importance included in the 20-year Ecoregional Conservation Plan drawn up by WWF and approved by the governments of all the countries on the greater Caucasus bio-corridor. This example clearly shows that funding can take various forms and combine public and private structures.

promoting protection and restoration of biological interconnections, particularly in Central and Eastern European countries.
The nature management plan for Central and Eastern European countries for the 2005-2008 period brings together the projects supported by the Netherlands in various fields, and is underpinned by the concept of biological corridors. The first lines of the action plan note that there are ecological links between Western and Eastern Europe, and that the Netherlands, like other European countries, has a responsibility with regard to conservation and the promotion of sustainable use of nature in Central and Eastern Europe.

The action plan thus makes it possible to finance the development of national biodiversity conservation plans or strategies, the establishment of ecological networks and the integration of the environment into other policies. It also provides scope for promoting effective protection of specific types of area, such as wetlands, coastal zones and forests. Migration routes are a key focus, as is the promotion of a sustainable relationship between agriculture and environmental management.

Tax incentives

Tax incentives could contribute usefully to the establishment of European ecological networks by making it easier to fund the necessary technical measures. Without having any undue effect on tax revenue, tax concessions – even modest ones – can facilitate changes in behaviour and help in creating a conservation culture.

However, a study carried out by the Council of Europe in 2004 showed that tax incentives aimed at promoting the conservation of biodiversity at pan-European level are insufficiently developed, and do not at present make a targeted contribution to strengthening ecological networks (Shine, 2005). There are considerable disparities between countries, and existing measures are generally fragmentary and insufficiently integrated within environmental protection measures.

Conclusion

It is through an articulation of numerous initiatives, combining international, national, regional and local dimensions, legal approaches to biodiversity and sectoral measures, from North-Western Europe to Central Asia, that PEEN is steadily taking shape.

Political recognition of PEEN, whether acting as initiator, orchestrator or catalyst, has certainly had a multiplier effect on development and support of initiatives on ecological networks at various scales across the continent. Whether within administrations from different sectors in the same country, between authorities from different countries or regions, between managers of transboundary protected areas or in dialogue with local populations, co-operation is a key element for the success of ecological networks and PEEN in particular.

Within the European Union, although still limited to identification and conservation of core areas, the implementation of the Natura 2000 network represents one of the most advanced processes for a transboundary ecological network, contributing to PEEN. Several other networks of protected sites coexist within Europe as a whole, such as Emerald, Ramsar Sites and Biosphere Reserves. International networks of sites, complemented by national networks of sites, are extremely important for practical implementation of the Pan-European Ecological Network. As well as constituting core areas, they also play a role in promoting sustainable development, including on the edges of protected areas.

In addition to (core) areas, many of which will be protected under European or international conservation laws, the Pan-European Ecological Network will also comprise buffer zones and corridors. Nationally protected areas will be essential in safeguarding appropriate management of these elements. It is also important to emphasize the ecological role played by certain sites that may not necessarily be protected, but are of considerable biological value, all of which are additional areas that contribute to the objectives of the Pan-European Ecological Network. This is true, for example, of the areas identified as 'Important Bird Areas', 'Important Plant Areas', 'Prime Butterfly Areas', 'High Nature Value Farming Areas' and 'High Nature Value Forests'. Also, natural rivers and coastlines are extremely important in maintaining ecological connectivity and as such are considered to be part of PEEN. The extent to which these non-protected areas are managed in a sustainable way will determine whether or not they will be able to maintain their ecological functionality and be an operational part of PEEN.

The European Union is making a particularly important contribution to projects aimed at developing the Pan-European Ecological Network, and examples of national co-operation all encourage consideration to be given to spatial links throughout Europe. The funding mechanisms set up in a number of countries for ecological network projects are complemented by the pooling of experience in relation to the concept of ecological networks, thereby facilitating the development of national and international ecological corridors.

Almost extinct species for a while but again very numerous, cormorants do compete with fishermen on their working places. Due to not water-tight feathers, they have to dry them at wind or sun.

D. Aubort

CHAPTER IV

General conclusion

Stoat (Mustela erminea)

"We endorse
the Pan-European

Biological and Landscape Diversity Strategy (…) as a framework for the conservation of biological and landscape diversity (…). We call for the promotion of nature protection, both inside and outside protected areas, by implementing the European Ecological Network, a physical network of core areas linked by corridors and supported by buffer zones or other appropriate measures, thus facilitating the dispersal and migration of species".

Twelve years have passed since the Ministers for Environment and Heads of Delegation of the Region of the United Nations Economic Commission for Europe (UNECE) made this solemn undertaking at the end of the third encounter, « An Environment for Europe » in Sofia in 1995.

In Kyiv, during the last Ministerial Conference, the representatives of the 51 governments present expressed the wish to adopt the appropriate measures and intensify their efforts to improve the global environment. They reiterated their political

Pine marten

responsibility vis-à-vis the millennium goal of halting the loss of biodiversity by 2010 and undertook to provide the necessary resources for the setting up of a pan-European ecological network (PEEN).

As a central component of the Pan-European Biological and Landscape Diversity Strategy adopted in 1995, PEEN is now regarded by European States as a key instrument for conserving and managing species, ecosystems, habitats and landscapes, within a global approach to spatial planning that is harmonious and contributes to the sustainable development of the peoples of Europe. It has also become a major instrument for implementing the Convention on Biological Diversity in Europe.

The protocol adopted in Kyiv sets out three successive implementation phases between now and 2010 :
• design and development of national action plans and ecological networks;
• formulation and implementation of appropriate plans for managing the components of the national ecological networks;
• mainstreaming PEEN in sectoral policies.

The results obtained so far provide several points of satisfaction.

A genuine framework for strategic co-operation

Major progress has been made, especially since the Kyiv Conference in ensuring that PEEN status can become a genuine system which, even though still only partially developed, is expressed in practical action at international, national, regional and local levels, and inducing member countries to take account of biological connectivity in their policies, legal systems and institutions.

The usefulness of PEEN is now more widely recognised by the public authorities, at Pan-European level; this major political reality has genuinely established itself in recent years.
• Through a modern response to the challenges of sustainable development, PEEN fulfils one of the latter's main functions, namely encouraging and facilitating international co-operation where the causes, or indeed the effects, of biological and landscape diversity loss lie outside the countries affected, and usually lie beyond their national boundaries.

• The enlargement of the European Union to ten further countries in 2004 has undoubtedly facilitated progress since the Kyiv Conference, and this progress should be pursued in the run-up to a further enlargement to the four current candidate countries.

• The process undertaken contributes to the implementation in Europe of the CBD's thematic work programmes, especially on protected areas promoting the creation of network systems of national and regional protected areas, which must be effectively managed and ecologically representative in order to conserve the biodiversity of ecosystems, habitats and biomes.

• In its present state, PEEN already provides the governments of European countries with a political framework for action at all levels, namely local, regional, national and international, enabling them to move towards sustainable socio-economic development while ensuring conservation of the biological and landscape diversity on which that development is partly based.

• Many international networks of protected areas and international instruments (eg. HELCOM, OSPAR, Alpine Convention, European Landscape Convention, European Outline Convention on Transfrontier Co-operation between regional authorities) are involved in conserving biological and landscape diversity in Europe. Many countries have adopted their own national institutional, legal land technical mechanisms, adapting the ecological networks to the prevailing national conditions. In Europe, the NATURA 2000 Network aims to link up all the sites of European interest in European Union member States, while the Emerald Network covers sites in European Union non-Member States.

• All these systems are helping towards the implementation of PEEN, in accordance with cultural diversity and the various political and methodological approaches specific to the Pan-European area.

• Above all, the effects of the biological and landscape diversity loss in Europe usually reach beyond the national boundaries; this is the case with transboundary pollution and climate change. PEEN provides decision-makers with a technical tool to identify the synergies needed and ensure overall coherence of their policies through international co-operation and common approaches.

• The principal value of PEEN lies in making available to countries involved in the Strategy a single monitoring and co-ordination mechanism that is sufficiently flexible to meet their respective expectations, in accordance with subsidiarities and specific, regional, national and local characteristics.

The composition of the network

PEEN relies on the existence and conservation of functional ecological links between its component elements. Accordingly, the identification of these components is a crucial factor in setting up PEEN.

In this context, the progress made since the Kyiv Conference is apparent at three levels, in terms of both concepts and implementation.

Designating the components of the Pan-European Ecological Network

• In addition to the numerous areas of international and/or national importance designated to date, which form the basic frame of the network that the PEEN process has

Killer Whale (N)

often catalysed or facilitated, there has also been appreciable progress in conceptual terms on the definition of PEEN's components.

• The various methodological approaches are currently converging towards a standard conception of the network, including on the difficult problem of ecological corridors. Practical responses to this issue have included a variety of measures, sectoral policies (eg agriculture and forestry), conditional recognition mechanisms (eg eco-certification of woods), financial arrangements (eg agri-environmental measures and eco-conditionality) and construction of appropriate infrastructures (eg wildlife bridges and dam structures), or, depending on the individual case, concepts taking account of different forms of ecological connectivity (eg open spaces along watercourses and the bio-geographical approach).

• These experiments conducted in the various countries show that the « ecological corridor » concept must be considered pragmatically and flexibly as part of an obligation to produce the specific result of maintaining economical connectivity around the nodal areas, using either a territorially-based technical approach or a more political procedure, as appropriate.

Cartographical representation of the Pan-European Ecological Network

The effort to draw up Europe-wide maps of PEEN began in 2000. An indicative map of PEEN in the countries of Central and Eastern Europe was presented in Kyiv. The process has been completed in Central, Eastern and South-Eastern Europe; it is continuing in the North-West. Furthermore, major initiatives are under way in Central Asia and the Caucasus, as well as in the entire territory of Russian Federation.

The cartography has indicative value; it was based on knowledge of the protected areas and the distribution of habitats and species considered to be of Pan-European interest. It is geared to facilitating the work under way at national level and stimulating the creation of PEEN.

Managing the components of the Pan-European Ecological Network

In accordance with the commitments entered into in Kyiv, conservation measures are applied in most of the PEEN nodal areas, and the need to ensure ecological connectivity between these areas is increasingly being considered in all national and regional public programmes. Evidence of this trend is provided by the numerous projects launched by local authorities, and especially the local communities, to promote the creation and management of local networks (eg green belts and corridors, inter-municipal planning and development strategies and inter-municipal development programmes) demonstrating that ecological connectivity between PEEN components is increasingly taken into account. There is also a trend towards joint management of these components within the international framework, through co-operation between the institutional players on the basis of various instruments:

• legal instruments governed by international law (eg Conventions for the protection of the Rhine and Danube, Alpine Convention, Benelux Convention and Trilateral Agreement on the Wadden Sea), some of which explicitly mention PEEN (eg Convention on the Protection and Sustainable Development of the Carpathians), and EU Law instruments (eg the Water Framework Directive and the FFH and Birds Directives), as well as instruments of domestic law (e.g. nature protection laws in Germany, Estonia, Hungary, Czech Republic and Slovakia);

• institutional instruments linked to international recognition of transboundary or contiguous areas (eg Biosphere reserves, European Diploma for Protected Areas, and the Ramsar areas);

• technical instruments comprising special projects (eg Green Belts, Caucasus Initiative, Danube Green Corridor, Central Asian ECONET and Regiobogen);

• multilateral financial instruments (eg Global Environment Fund, Ramsar small subsidies fund and UNESCO MAB Programme), EU instruments (eg LIFE Nature Programmes, INTERREG, EAGGF, ERDF, EAFRD, LEADER, PHARE, SAPARD and ISPA) and bilateral instruments linked to development aid (eg WWF, Germany and Netherlands).

These factors make for a great variety of mechanisms suited to a networked approach, and consequently for the high flexibility of PEEN, which demonstrates its adaptability to the many local characteristics of the Pan-European area.

However, all these initiatives should not delude us. There is still a great deal to be done to guarantee the complete functionality of these networks and of PEEN in particular, before the 2010 objective is fully attained:

Integrating the Pan-European Ecological Network in sectoral policies

Among the future aims of the strategy process the Environment Ministers of the region of the Economic Commission for Europe (UNECE) have included the need for environmental mainstreaming within sectoral policies. Such mainstreaming constitutes the most complete form of the process currently under way.

While progress has been made since the last Ministerial Conference, it remains limited, and the States' commitment to ensure that PEEN provides advice, by 2008, for all major spatial development plans and for the activities of the economic and financial sectors has not yet been fulfilled. The Kyiv Declaration concluded that results in this area had been poor, and it is without doubt here that progress has been least significant since the last Conference.

• In agriculture and forestry, specific consideration of biological and landscape diversity in European agricultural policies is of recent date. Over the last fifteen years this approach has been mainly reflected in a review of the Common Agricultural Policy and modernisation of the farming subsidies aid scheme; the following action may be mentioned inter alia:

• agri-environmental measures to encourage environment-friendly farming methods: such measures were introduced in the EU Member States from 1991 onwards but actually began in earnest with European Regulation No. 207/92 requiring Member States to implement the measures;

• eco-conditionality, which makes individual subsidies subject to environment-friendly criteria;

• the multifunctionality concept, which is based on the idea that agriculture fulfils a variety of functions, including environmental, biological and landscape ones.

• the principle of decoupling whereby the aid allocated is no longer proportionate to the quantities produced.

These developments in EU Member States were confirmed in 2005 by the new Community Regulation on rural development. They also provided the basis to some extent for Community assistance to other European countries and the national agricultural reforms that followed the political upheavals accompanying the birth of new European States.

However, it has not yet been shown that such mechanisms really help to conserve biological and landscape diversity.

• Moreover, few of the Resolutions of the High-Level Pan-European Conference on Agriculture and Biodiversity: Towards Integrating Biological and Landscape Diversity for Sustainable Agriculture in Europe (Paris, 2003) have so far actually been implemented. Nor has the key objective adopted in Kyiv, namely completing the inventory of all areas of high natural value in the agricultural ecosystems of the pan-European region by 2006, been attained as yet. This also applies to some of the other Kyiv objectives for 2008 in this field, viz.:

• managing a large proportion of the areas surveyed using biodiversity-friendly methods, through such appropriate mechanisms as rural enhancement

Bearded vulture

instruments, agri-environmental programmes and biological agriculture, particularly with a view to safeguarding the economic and ecological viability of these areas;

• taking into consideration conservation and sustainable use of biodiversity in all systems of subsidy and financial incentive for agriculture in the Pan-European region.

• With regard to forests, the key objectives defined in Kyiv have been largely reached: namely, by 2008, helping to implement the enlarged work programme of the Convention on Biological Diversity relating to forest biodiversity in the pan-European region by, inter alia:

• implementing the objectives and activities of the framework for co-operation between the Ministerial Conference on the Protection of Forests in Europe and the Strategy;

• implementing national forest programmes in line with the approach adopted by the Ministerial Conference on the Protection of Forests in Europe (MCPFE) to national programmes in Europe (Vienna Conference, 2003);

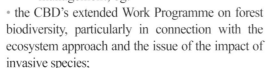

Chub

• implementing an ecosystem-friendly approach.

• Effective international co-operation has developed over the last few years between the Strategy process and the MCPFE, concentrating on a limited number of priority themes decided in agreement between both mechanisms:
• the ecosystem approach;
• protected forest areas;
• implementation of forest regulations with due regard to the conservation of biodiversity;
• deforestation.

Principles and Recommendations have been adopted in this framework, taking into account the work conducted in other international fora involved in forestry management, eg:
• the CBD's extended Work Programme on forest biodiversity, particularly in connection with the ecosystem approach and the issue of the impact of invasive species;
• the Intergovernmental Working Group on Forests;
• the United Nations Forum on Forests;
• the WSSD implementation strategy.

It is important to pursue this programme-based co-operation between the two mechanisms and develop current thinking, ensuring on the one hand that the decisions taken at PEEN level and the countries participating in the process are implemented and on the other hand that these actions are consistent with community forest policy.

• In the area of transport, results are mixed and the drive for integration remains singularly inadequate, while air transport has a direct impact on certain ecosystem-related services linked to air quality and, indirectly, to climate change, and land and river transport clearly affects the conservation of biological and landscape diversity, positively or negatively depending on the case:

• land transport has an impact on fragmentation of the territory in general, and through management of road and rail verges and embankments and their related amenities;
• river transport affects watercourse development and management, as well as hydrological regimes and the state of aquatic ecosystems;
• road, rail and river transport leave marks on the landscape.

• The diverse responses to these issues to date include: ensuring consideration of biological and landscape diversity in the choice of location and design of transport infrastructures; applying ecological management and maintenance methods to infrastructures and related facilities; demolishing dams or equipping them with crossing facilities; creating passageways for wildlife over and under roads and railways; maintaining open spaces along watercourses; the Water Framework Directive and the related national legislation, promoting uniform management of water resources and the ecosystem approach; international Conventions governing the specific issue of transport and navigation (eg the transport protocol to the Alpine Convention, the International Convention for the Protection of the Rhine, etc).

The international and EU approaches to developing the Trans-European transport network will in future have to ensure that the declared priority of integrating the environmental dimension in this network is reflected in practical action, devised according to the sensitivity of ecological network components in general and of PEEN in particular.

• Many other public policies interfere with the proper functioning of ecological networks, conservation of their component features and maintenance of biological connectivity:
• energy policy choices often have a specific effect on the proper functioning of ecological networks; this applies to the production of hydro-electric energy by means of dams across watercourses, wind energy using infrastructures that have a major impact on bird migration, or the production of biofuels, which directly has a direct bearing on agricultural policy and promotes crops at high environmental cost;
• tourism exerts pressure on ecosystems; it disturbs species and damages habitats, and can also disrupt biological connectivity, in extreme cases leading to the disappearance of particularly sensitive species and habitats;
• water policies that overlook the quantitative and qualitative state of water resources cause damage

to aquatic habitats and undermine numerous ecosystem services provided by them (eg prevention of flooding, retention and maintenance of water quality, etc).

• Conversely, ecological networks are a potential source of socio-economic wealth, and their conservation provides guarantees for sustainable development:
• the quality of landscapes, fauna and flora, is an asset for the development of tourist activities;
• proper watercourse management limits the destructive effects of flooding and the consequences of prolonged drought on water consumption;
• international co-operation on sensible management of natural resources helps to harmonise relations between the countries involved, enhances their security and optimises ecological services.

• Generally speaking, much remains to be done to integrate environmental considerations into these sectoral and vertical policies, and more specifically to take ecological networks into account when framing and implementing such policies. In future it will be especially important to ensure that those considerations are integrated at local level, in conjunction with the public authorities concerned.

Still some way to go

Today, the PEEN is at a critical stage in its implementation.

Since Kyiv, the idea has taken shape and numerous initiatives have made it possible to give practical expression to what yesterday was no more than a concept relying on political will alone. PEEN is now assuming different tangible forms and representations and it already constitutes a coherent framework, founded on a common, shared vision of sustainable development in Europe.

The PEEN concept highlights various elements which underpin the implementation of ecological networks: knowledge of functional aspects of landscapes and ecological infrastructures, management in space and time, compliance with legal frameworks and networking among people.

This report shows how much progress has been made in various fields. It also highlights where gaps remain. Thus, even if it is increasing, the number of protected areas is still insufficient to ensure long term conservation of core biodiversity areas. Furthermore, the efficiency

of existing protected areas which is closely linked to protection and/ or management schemes is often jeopardised by exogenous and endogenous pressures on these areas. In addition, assessment mechanisms to monitor the efficiency of protected areas are often lacking. The work of the CBD protected areas group should provide common guidelines on future action for European countries.

Cooperation mechanisms set up under the PEEN framework may help to improve the effectiveness of international legislation which now offers many useful instruments for biodiversity conservation.

But it is without doubt in the field of biodiversity mainstreaming into sectoral policies that efforts have to be enhanced.

The lessons learnt in Europe in the PEEN context on ecological connectivity make it possible to envisage consolidating the process on existing foundations, as well as exchanges of experiences with other regions of the world.

Common crossbill

As a tool for sustainable development, the Pan-European Ecological Network needs to be backed by strong political will so as to continue to stimulate ecological connectivity initiatives.

Rhodes (GR)

R. Clerc

ANNEXES

Scarce copper (Heodes virgaurae)

The history of the Pan-European Ecological Network's political process

1990   The European Conservation Strategy prepared by the Council of Europe is endorsed.

1991   The First Ministerial Conference 'Environment for Europe' (Dobris, Czeck Republic) reviews the state of the environment in Europe and launches dialogue on the nature and threats in Europe.

1992   EU Habitats Directive enters into force, Article 3 stating: 'A coherent European Ecological Network shall be set up under the title Natura 2000'.

1993   Lucerne Ministerial conference, the second meeting of the 'Environment for Europe' process.
A Pan-European Strategy is proposed in the Maastricht Conference's Declaration 'Conserving Europe's Natural Heritage' building upon the Bern Convention, the European Conservation Strategy, the Dobris and Lucerne Ministerial Conferences, the Rio Summit, CBD and other initiatives and programmes.

1994   The Council of Europe and ECNC, in co-operation with other national governmental and non-governmental organisations, decides to set up the Pan-European Biological and Landscape Diversity Strategy to support implementation of the CBD in Europe. One of its Action Themes is the establishment of the Pan-European Ecological Network.

The Monaco Declaration under the aegis of the Bern Convention and the Council of Europe recommends conducting research necessary to identify knowledgeably the constituent elements of biological diversity and therefore of ecological networks.

1995   The Pan-European Biological and Landscape Diversity Strategy is endorsed at the Third Ministerial Conference 'Environment for Europe' in Sofia, Bulgaria; 54 countries to date and all international governmental organisations and NGOs involved in nature conservation, biodiversity and environment protection in Europe are stakeholders in the Strategy. Following this decision a Council and Bureau of PEBLDS are established, creating an intergovernmental committee of experts to oversee the establishment of PEEN.

1998   The 'Green Backbone of Central and Eastern Europe' International Conference (Krakow, Poland) supports establishment of PEEN in Central and Eastern Europe.

At the Fourth 'Environment for Europe' Ministerial Conference in Aarhus, Denmark, the European governments issue a declaration welcoming progress made in the establishment of PEEN.

2000   First Intergovernmental conference 'Biodiversity in Europe' held in Riga, Latvia, with the aim of improving and enhancing regional co-operation and implementation of the CBD in Europe, through existing international frameworks and instruments, namely PEBLDS, the EC Biodiversity Strategy and other relevant biodiversity-related strategies.

2001   The European Commission's Action Plan for Natural Resources under the EC Biodiversity Strategy, emphasises the need to increase connectivity between Natura 2000 sites.

2002   The Second Intergovernmental conference 'Biodiversity in Europe' held in Budapest, Hungary, notes that including conservation and sustainable use of biodiversity in all relevant economic and financial sectors and policies and in spatial planning is key to sustainable development, in Europe and worldwide.
At the 6th Conference of the Parties of the CBD (COP 6), The Hague, The Netherlands, it is agreed to make protected areas as the central theme of COP 7.

The World summit on Sustainable Development in Johannesburg, South Africa, confirms support for the work of the CBD and decides to promote ecological networks in all regions of the world.

The IUCN Vth World Parks Congress, Durban, South Africa, addresses the issue of 'Benefits Beyond Boundaries' in protected area policies and management.
A Colloquy on marine and coastal ecological corridors is organised in Llandudno, Wales by the Council of Europe.

2003   The 5th Ministerial Conference 'Environment for Europe', Kyiv, Ukraine adopts a Ministerial Resolution on Biodiversity setting out specific targets and deadlines for the establishment of PEEN, as well as a Statement on PEEN.

PEBLDS decides to set up a European Coastal and Marine Ecological Network.

2004   Third Intergovernmental conference Biodiversity in Europe held in Madrid, Spain, focusing mainly on priority issues for the 7th Conference of the Parties to the Convention on Biological Diversity and on attaining the '2010 target, Countdown 2010 initiative launched.

COP7/CBD adopts a detailed Programme of Work on Protected Areas.

2005   10th Anniversary of the PEBLDS process celebrated in Strasbourg, France. Governments decide to enhance focus on political priorities, and to increase interactions with land use, business and financial sectors. The governments conclude that, although important progress has been made in implementing PEBLDS, natural areas, biodiversity and landscape are still declining in Europe.

2006   Fourth Intergovernmental conference Biodiversity in Europe held at Lake Plitvice, Croatia, designed to prepare for the COP8/CBD Conference, expresses inter alia a strong commitment to the implementation of PEEN.

COP8/CBD in Curitiba, Brazil, under the theme of protected areas, focuses on marine PAs, and redefines the Convention's role in relation to PAs in the high seas.

Activities contributing to the implementation of the Pan-European Ecological Network supported by the Pan-European biological and landscape diversity Strategy, 1997-2006

First Action Plan 1997-2000

Group I: high-priority projects:
- Evaluation of the state of progress and of criteria and methods for developing the Pan-European Ecological Network, including relevant parts of the coastal and marine ecological network and of the large carnivores network.
- Preparation of guidelines highlighting the above elements, including relevant elements of the coastal and marine ecological network and of the large carnivores network.
- Preparation of information booklet on the Pan-European Ecological Network and design of an information strategy.

Group II: lower priority projects:
- Development of national ecological networks in Central and Eastern Europe.
- Establishment of an integrated policy by means of wide-ranging consultation and contributions from local and regional authorities, NGOs and groups interested in developing national and regional ecological networks.
- Design of an information strategy with a view to successfully establishing the Pan-European Ecological Network.

Whale

Leopard :
present in Caucasus.
(Source: WWF Germany)

Second Rolling Programme of Work 2000-2006

- Endorsement of the PEEN declaration by the Kyiv Ministerial Conference.
- Support activities for the creation of national, regional and trans-national networks.
- Programmes of activities by the various partners engaged in PEEN implementation.
- Technical and scientific studies, seminars, joint meeting of PEEN and Emerald committees, co-operation with international institutions and legal instruments.
- Preparation of PEEN maps, documents, PowerPoint presentations, brochures.
- Seminars, studies, development of common PEEN activities with other sectors.
- Development of ECONETs in Ukraine, Romania, Belarus, Russia.
- Development and conservation of areas of importance for plants, birds and fauna generally.
- Conference on Marine and Coastal Biodiversity..
- Development of ECONET for long-term biodiversity conservation in the Central Asia Eco-regions.
- Development of a framework for regional co-operation on the protection and sustainable management of the Carpathians.
- Establishment of a Carpathian Network of Protected Areas.
- Feasibility study on the preparation of a legal instrument or an agreement.
- Creation of the Caucasus Green Corridor.
- Feasibility study on the preparation of a legal instrument for the protection of Central Asian mountain ecosystems.
- Preparation of guidelines for a handbook on ECONET: the European Experience as a contribution towards the development of a Global ECONET.
- Strengthening the network of nature conservation experts and organisations in the Balkans.
- Workshops on the implementation of PEEN in Central and Eastern European Countries (CEEC) and Newly Independent States (NIS).
- Report and Indicative PEEN map for CEEC.
- Indicative maps for Western Europe, 4 - Visegrad, NIS and the Balkans.
- Development of a Communication Strategy on PEEN based on stakeholder consultations.

The Kyiv Resolution on biodiversity targets

The aim to establish a Pan-European Ecological Network was reinforced in 2003 at the Fifth 'Environment for Europe' Ministerial Conference in Kyiv which led to an Action Plan to implement PEEN, then to the Kyiv Resolution on Biodiversity.

The proposed Europe-wide targets in the Resolution for stabilising biodiversity by 2010 were:

- taking effective action by 2008 to prevent human activities from damaging forests;
- finalising an inventory of all high-value natural areas in agriculture ecosystems by 2006 and ensuring that a substantial proportion of these areas are under biodiversity-sensitive management by 2008;
- integrating biodiversity issues into all financial subsidy and incentive schemes for agriculture in Europe by 2008;
- ensuring the speedy application of the Pan-European Ecological Network by identifying and mapping all core areas of high ecological value, as well as restoration areas, wildlife corridors and buffer zones, by 2006, and then adequately conserving all core areas by 2008;
- implementing an agreed strategy on alien invasive species in at least half of the region's countries by 2008; and
- increasing substantially public and private financial investments in biodiversity via partnerships with the finance and business sectors, establishing a coherent European programme on biodiversity monitoring and indicators, and implementing national communication, education and public awareness plans in at least half the region's countries, all by 2008.

The Resolution includes therefore among its targets the requirement for the implementation of PEEN and a statement that all countries agree to the PEEN targets:

- by 2006, the Pan-European Ecological Network (core areas, restoration areas, corridors and buffer zones, as appropriate) in all States of the pan European region will be identified and represented on coherent indicative European maps, as a European contribution towards a global ecological network;
- by 2008 all core areas of the Pan-European Ecological Network will be appropriately conserved;
- by 2008, PEEN guidelines will apply to all major national, regional and international land-use and planning policies, as well as to the relevant economic and financial sectors.

Members of the editorial committee for the preparation of the Pan-European Ecological Network's indicative maps and the assessment report

Dr Marie BONNIN, Université de Versailles Saint-Quentin, Institut de recherche pour le développement, CBED/UVSQ, 47 Bd Vauban, F78 Guyancourt, France, Tel: +33 (0)6 61 93 37 64, fax: +33 2 40 14 16 44, e-mail: marie.bonnin@ird.fr

Mr Peter BOS, Senior Executive Officer for International Nature Affairs, Ministry of Agriculture, Nature and Food Quality, Directorate for Nature, Postbus 20401, 2500 EK The Hague, Tel. +31 70 378 5529, fax +31 70 378 6146, e-mail p.w.bos@minlnv.nl

Mrs Hélène BOUGUESSA, Principal Administrative Assistant, Natural Heritage Division/ Division du Patrimoine naturel, Council of Europe/Conseil de l'Europe, F - 67075 STRASBOURG Cedex, France, Tel. +33 (0)3 88 41 22 64, fax +33 (0)3 88 41 37 51, e-mail helene.bouguessa@coe.int

Ms Agnes BRUSZIK, Project Manager, ECNC, Reitseplein 3, 5037 AA Tilburg (PO Box 90154, 5000 LG Tilburg), the Netherlands, Tel. +31 13 5944949 ; fax +31 13 5944945, e-mail : bruszik@ecnc.org

Mr Henri JAFFEUX, Chargé de mission, Direction Nature et Paysages, Ministère de l'Ecologie et du Développement durable, 20 avenue de Ségur, 75302 Paris 07 SP Tel. +33 (1) 42 19 19 14, fax + 33 (1) 42 19 19 98, e-mail : henri.jaffeux@ecologie.gouv.fr

Mrs Ilona JEPSENA, Administrator, DG ENV.B2, Nature and Biodiversity, European Commission, Avenue de Beaulieu 9, 1160 Brussels, Tel.+32 2 296 9149, Fax +32 2 299 0895, e-mail ilona.jepsena@cec.eu.int

Dr Robert JONGMAN, Alterra, Alterra Wageningen UR, PO box 47, 6700 AA Wageningen, The Netherlands, Tel: +31 (317) 474626, Fax: +31 (317) 419000, e-mail: rob.jongman@wur.nl

Mr Hervé LETHIER, EMC2I, consultant, Le Belvedere, Chemin de l'Observatoire, 1264 Saint Cergue, Suisse, Tel: +41 22 360 12 34, e-mail: herve.lethier@wanadoo.fr

Dr Jan PLESNIK, Deputy Director, Agency for Nature Conservation and Landscape Protection of the Czech Republic, Kališnická 4-6, CZ 130 23 PRAGUE 3
Tel. +420 2 2258 0562, fax +420 2 2258 0012, e-mail : jan_plesnik@nature.cz

Mrs Jasminka RADOVIC, Institute for Nature Protection, Savska cesta 41/23, 10144, pp.50, Zagreb, Tel., +385 1 4866 189, Fax 385 1 4866 171

Dr Dominique RICHARD, Directrice adjointe/Deputy Director, Centre thématique européen sur la diversité biologique (CTE/DB)/European Topic Centre on Biological Diversity (ETC/BD, Muséum national d'Histoire naturelle, 57 rue Cuvier, 75231 Paris Cedex 07, France, Tel. +33 (1) 40 79 38 70, fax +33 (1) 40 79 38 67, e-mail drichard@mnhn.fr

Mrs Sandra RIENTJES, Head of Programme Development, Deputy Executive Director, European Centre for Nature Conservation (ECNC)/Centre européen pour la Conservation de la Nature (CECN), Reitseplein 3, 5037 AA Tilburg (PO Box 90154, 5000 LG Tilburg), the Netherlands, Tel. +31 (13) 5944944, fax +31 (13) 5944945, e-mail rientjes@ecnc.org

Mr Marc ROEKAERTS, consultant, Ringlaan 57, 3530 HOUTHALEN, Belgium
Tel. +32 11 60 42 34, fax +32 11 60 24 59, E-mail marc.roekaerts@eureko.be

Mr Gianluca SILVESTRINI, Head of the Natural Heritage Division/Division du Patrimoine naturel, Council of Europe/Conseil de l'Europe, F - 67075 STRASBOURG Cedex, France, Tel. +33 (0)3 88 4135 59, E-mail gianluca.silvestrini@coe.int

Dr Jan-Willem SNEEP, Chair of the STRA-REP, Director of the Dutch National Parc Foundation, Laan van Nieuw, Oost-Indië, 131-133, 2593 BM, The Hague
Tel. +31 (0)70 378 5255, fax +31 (0)70 378 6175, e-mail : sneep@nationaalpark.nl

Dr Nikolay SOBOLEV, Head of Programme, Biodiversity Conservation Center, Office 2, 41 Vavilova Str., 117312 Moscow, Tel: +7 495 124 50 22, fax: + 7 495 124 71 78, e-mail: laecol@online.ru

Mrs Rania SPYROPOULOU, European Environment Agency, Project Manager for Nature and Biodiversity, Kongens Nytorv 6, 1050 Copenhagen –K, Denmark
Tel. +45 33 36 71 2, e-mail rania.spyropoulou@eea.eu.int

Mr Jacques STEIN, Objectif 2010, Ministère de la Région wallonne, Direction de la nature, Division de la Nature et des Forêts, Avenue Prince de Liège, 15, 5100 Jambes (Namur)
Tel. +32 81 33 58 60 /+32 477 26 60 46, fax +32 81 33 58 22, e-mail j.stein@mrw.wallonie.be

Mr Andrew TERRY, Scientific Adviser, World Conservation Union (IUCN)/Union mondiale pour la nature (UICN), Bureau Régional pour l'Europe/Régional Office for Europe, Boulevard Louis Schmidt 64, 1040 Brussels, Belgium, Tel. +32 (0) 2 732 82 99
fax + 32 (0) 2 732 94 99

Mr Jean-Louis WEBER, European Environment Agency, Project Manager, Environmental Accounting Analyst, Kongens Nytorv 6, 1050 Copenhagen – DK, Denmark
Tel. +45 33 36 72 45, fax +45 33 36 72 93, e-mail jean-louis.weber@eea.eu.int

Mr Rob WOLTERS, Executive Director, European Centre for Nature Conservation (ECNC)/ Centre européen pour la Conservation de la Nature (CECN), PO Box 90154, 5000 LG TILBURG, Netherlands, Tel: +31 13 5944 944, fax: +31 13 5944 945, e-mail: wolters@ecnc.org

Alpine sea Holly

Bibliography

BENNETT, G., 2002. Guidelines on the application of existing international instruments in developing the Pan-European Ecological Network, Council of Europe, Nature and Environment Series, No. 124, ISBN 92-871-4935-6, 98 p.

BENNETT G., 2004. Integrating Biodiversity Conservation and Sustainable Use: Lessons Learned from Ecological Networks, IUCN Gland, Switzerland, and Cambridge, United Kingdom.

BICKMORE, C., 2001. Code of practice for the introduction of biological and landscape diversity considerations into the transport sector, Council of Europe, Nature and Environment Series, No 131, ISBN 92-871-5115-6, 68 p.

BIODIVERSITY CONSERVATION CENTER, 2006. The draft overview map of the Russian Ecological Network (RUSECONET) by the end 2006. Cartographical Database on Federal SPNA of Russia, 2002-2005. World Resource Institute, International Socio-Ecological Union, Biodiversity Conservation Center.

BONNIN Marie, 2004. Les aspects juridiques des corridors biologiques, vers un troisième temps de la conservation de la nature, Thèse de doctorat, Université de Nantes, 586 p.

BIRÓ, E., I. BOUWMA and V. GROBELNIK (Eds), 2006. Indicative map of the Pan-European Ecological Network in South-Eastern Europe. Technical background document. – Tilburg, ECNC–European Centre for Nature Conservation, ECNC technical report series, in print.

BOUWMA, I.M., JONGMAN R.H.G. & R.O. BUTOVSKY (eds), 2002. The Indicative map of the Pan-European Ecological Network for Central and Eastern Europe – Technical background document. (ECNC technical report series). ECNC, Tilburg, The Netherlands/Budapest Hungary.

BRUNNER R., 2002. Identification of the most important transboundary protected areas in Central and Eastern Europe, Council of Europe, Nature and Environment Series, No 128, ISBN 92-871-4991-7, 40 p.

CLERGEAU, P., DESIRE, G., Biodiversité, paysage et aménagement : du corridor à la zone de connexion biologique, Mappemonde n°55, 1999.3

CONFERENCE ON BIOLOGICAL DIVERSITY (CBD), 2005. Programme of Work on Protected Areas, Goals 1.2 and 1.3, Review of experience with ecological networks, corridors and buffer zones.

COUNCIL OF EUROPE, PNUE & ECNC, 1996. The Pan-European Biological and Landscape Diversity Strategy, ISBN 90-802482-4-X, 50 p.

COUNCIL OF EUROPE, 1997. Incentive measures for the voluntary creation and management of protected areas, Council of Europe, Environment Encounters Series, No 35, bilingual version, ISBN 92-871-3381-6, 266 p.

COUNCIL OF EUROPE, 1998. The Pan-European Ecological Network, Questions & Answers Series, No 4, 28 p.

COUNCIL OF EUROPE, 2000. General guidelines for the development of the Pan-European ecological network, Nature and Environment Series, No 107, ISBN 92-871-4335-8, 56 p.

COUNCIL OF EUROPE, 2000. Nature does not have any borders : towards transfrontier ecological networks, 1st symposium of the Pan-European Ecological Network, Environmental Encounters Series, No 44, bilingual version, 178 p.

COUNCIL OF EUROPE, 2000. Workshop on the ecological corridors for invertebrates – strategies of dispersal and recolonisation in today's agricultural and forestry landscapes, Environmental Encounters Series No 45, bilingual version, ISBN 92-871-4375-7, 168 p.

COUNCIL OF EUROPE, 2001. Biological diversity and environmental law, Environmental Encounters, No 48, bilingual version, ISBN 92-871-4593-8, 172 p.

COUNCIL OF EUROPE, 2001. The partnership of local and regional authorities in the conservation of biological and landscape diversity, 2nd PEEN Symposium, Environmental Encounters Series, No 50, bilingual version, ISBN 92-871-4610-1, 176 p.

COUNCIL OF EUROPE, 2003. Integration of biodiversity into sectoral policies, Questions & Answers Series, No 7, 36 p.

COUNCIL OF EUROPE, 2003. High-level Pan-European conference « Agriculture and biodiversity : towards integrating biological and landscape diversity for sustainable agriculture in Europe », Environmental Encounters Series No 53, bilingual version, ISBN 92-871-5115-1, 297 p.

COUNCIL OF EUROPE, 2003. Fragmentation of habitats and ecological corridors, 3rd PEEN Symposium, Environmental Encounters Series No 54, bilingual version, ISBN 92-871-5178-4, 111 p.

COUNCIL OF EUROPE, 2003. Marine and coastal ecological corridors, Environmental Encounters Series No 55, bilingual version, ISBN 92-871-5194-6, 115 p.

COUNCIL OF EUROPE, 2004. High-level Pan-European Conference on "Agriculture and Biodiversity" – Compendium of background reports, Nature and Environment Series, No 133, ISBN 92-871-5856-8, 758 p.

COUNCIL OF EUROPE, 2004. Marine and coastal biodiversity and protected areas, 4th PEEN Symposium, Environmental Encounters Series No 56, bilingual version, 273 p.

COUNCIL OF EUROPE, 2005. Pan-European Ecological Network in forests : conservation of biodiversity and sustainable development, 5th PEEN symposium, Environmental Encounters Series No 57, bilingual version, 220 p.

COUNCIL OF EUROPE, 2006. 40th anniversary of the European Diploma : a network for nature and people, Seminar of managers of areas holding the European Diploma of Protected Areas, Environmental Encounters Series No 62, bilingual version, 198 p.

CORSI, F., BOITANI, L., SINIBALDI, I., 2002. Ecological corridors and species: large carnivores in the Alpine region, Nature and Environment Series No 127, ISBN 92-871-4989-5, 24 p.

EEA (EUROPEAN ENVIRONMENT AGENCY), 1999. Environment in the European Union at the turn of the century – Luxembourg, Office for Official Publications of the European Communities

EEA (EUROPEAN ENVIRONMENT AGENCY), 2005. The European Environment: State and Outlook 2005. Copenhagen.

FOPPEN, R.P.B., I.M. BOUWMA, J.T.R. KALKHOVEN, J. DIRKSEN & S. VAN OPSTAL, 2000. Corridors of the Pan-European Ecological Network. Produced by ECNC together with Alterra, the Dutch Ministry for Agriculture, Nature Management and Fisheries, and the Council of Europe, Tilburg, European Centre for Nature Conservation. ECNC Technical Report Series, ISBN 90-76762-05-8.

HANSKI, I., and M. GILPIN, 1991. Metapopulation dynamics: brief history and conceptual domain. Biological Journal of the Linnean Society 42:3–16.

HESLENFELD, J., LIÉVIN, J., MIELCHEN, V., PICKAVER, A., SALMAN, A. AND DAVID, L., 2003. Corridors and ecosystems: coastal and marine areas, Council of Europe, Nature and Environment Series, No 134, ISBN 92-871-5258-6, 48 p.

HINDMARCH, C. and KIRBY, J., 2002. Corridors for birds within a Pan-European Ecological Network, Council of Europe, Nature and Environment Series, No 123, ISBN 92-871-4907-6, 50 p.

JONGMAN, R.H.G. and KAMPHORST, D., 2002. Ecological corridors in land use planning and development policies, Council of Europe, Nature and Environment Series, No 125, ISBN 92-871-4936-4, 56 p.

JONGMAN, R.H.G., 2004. The context and concept of ecological networks. In: R.H.G. Jongman & G. Pungetti (Eds) Ecological Networks and Greenways: Concept, Design, Implementation. – Cambridge, Cambridge University Press.

JONGMAN, R.H.G, KRISTIANSEN & ECNC, 2001. National and regional approaches for ecological networks in Europe, Council of Europe, Nature and Environment Series, No 110, ISBN 92-871-4781-7, 95 p.

KLEMM (DE), Cyril, 1992. Conservation of natural habitats outside protected areas – legal analysis, Council of Europe, Nature and Environment Series, No 56, ISBN 92-871-1997-X, 59 p.

KUIJKEN, E., and DE BLUST, G., 2003. The restoration of sites and ecological corridors in the framework of building up a Pan-European Ecological Network, with examples of best practices from European countries, Council of Europe Nature and Environment Series, N° 135, ISBN 92-871-5276-4, 70 p.

LEVINS, R. (1969) Some demographic and genetic consequences of environmental heterogeneity for biological control. Bulletin of the Entomology Society of America, 71, 237-240.

MACARTHUR & WILSON, 1967. The Theory of Island Biogeography: ISBN 0-691-08836-5.

McDONNELL, M., A paradigm Shift, Urban ecosystems, Springer Netherlands, Vol 1, n°2, Juin 1997, p. 85-86.

MOUGENOT C. et ROUSSEL L., 2002. Ecological network and local authorities – sociological instruments, Council of Europe, Nature and Environment Series, No 126, ISBN 92-871-4996-8, 30 p.

OFFICE FEDERAL DE L'ENVIRONNEMENT, DES FORETS ET DU PAYSAGE (OFEFP), 2004. Réseau écologique national REN, Rapport final. Cahier de l'environnement n° 373. SRU-373-F ; Cartes : SRU-373-TD.

PERELADOVA, O., KREVER, V., SHESTAKOV, A., eds. WWF, 2006. ECONET Central Asia, 48 p.

PULLIAM, H. R. 1988. Sources, Sinks, and Population regulation. American Naturalist 132 :652-661.

RIENTJES, S. 2000. Communicating nature conservation. ISBN 90-802482-9-0. Tilburg, European Centre for Nature Conservation. ECNC Technical report series.

RIENTJES, S. & ROUMELIOTI, K. 2003. Support for ecological networks in European nature conservation: an indicative social map. Tilburg, ECNC.

RODOMAN, B. B. 1974. Polarisation of landscape as a management agent in the protection of biosphere and recreational resources. In Resursy, Sreda, Rasselenije, pp.150-63 Nauka, Moscow.

SADELER (DE), N., FAUCONNIER, J.M., KURSTJENS, G., BERTHOUD, G., COOPER, R.J., 2003. Studies on transport and biological and landscape diversity, Council of Europe, Nature and Environment Series, No 132, ISBN 92-871-5278-0, 136 p.

SHINE Clare (2005), Using tax incentives to conserve and enhance biodiversity in Europe/Les incitations fiscales et la protection de la biodiversité en Europe (version bilingue), Conseil de l'Europe,Série Sauvegarde de la nature, n° 143, ISBN 928-871-5780-4, 110 p.
STEIN J, WOLF (DE) P., 1995. Communes et biodiversité, Ministère de la region wallonne et Conseil de l'Europe, 121 pages.

VAN DER SLUIS, T. M., BLOEMEN, M. and BOUWMA I. M., 2004. European corridors: Strategies for corridor development for target species

WENGER, Edith, 2002. Guidelines for the constitution of ecological river networks, Council of Europe, Nature and Environment Series, No 129, ISBN 92-871-4993-3, 44 p.

WWF Caucasus Programme, 2006.http://www.caucasus-conference.org/en/background. htm#ecp

NB. : THE PUBLICATIONS ISSUED BY THE COUNCIL OF EUROPE ARE AVAILABLE ON THE WEB SITE http://www.coe.int/T/E/ Cultural co-operation/Environment/.

Glossary

Biological diversity

The variability among living organisms from all sources including, inter alia, terrestrial, marine and other aquatic ecosystems and the ecological complexes of which they are part; this includes diversity within species, between species and of ecosystems (Article 2 of the Convention on Biological Diversity).

Buffer zone

A functional protecting strip surrounding core areas and restoration sites

Core areas

Areas that are coherent as regards soil composition, hydrology and climate, that are ecologically integrated (there are functional relations between the different parts of the area, functional as regards the main ecosystems of the core area), that are built up of natural, almost natural, semi-natural or multi-functional ecosystems (or a mosaic of these ecosystems) and their actual ecological value is of European significance.

Ecological corridors

Corridors should contribute (directly or indirectly, on a medium term or on a longer term) to the protection or the ecological functioning of ecosystems or species of European importance

Ecological network

An ecological network is a system of representative core areas, corridors, stepping stones and buffer zones designed and managed in such a way as to preserve biodiversity, maintain or restore ecosystem services and allow a suitable and sustainable use of natural resources through interconnectivity of its physical elements with the landscape and existing social/institutional structures (based on SBSTTA 9) STRA CO (2004) 10

Landscape diversity

The formal expression of the numerous relations existing in a given period between the individual or a society and a topographically defined territory, the appearance of which is the result of the action, over time, of natural and human factors and a combination of both (Council of Europe Draft Recommendation on the Integrated Conservation of Cultural Landscape Areas as part of Landscape Policies).

Pan-European Ecological Network

The Pan-European Ecological Network will be the operational framework within which many of the strategic and priority actions will be taken. It is both a physical network through which ecosystems, habitats, species, landscapes and other natural features of European importance are conserved, and a coordinating mechanism through which the partners in the Strategy can develop and implement cooperative actions. It will build on a variety of existing initiatives, including Natura 2000, the European network of Biogenetic Reserves, the EECONET concept, the Bern Convention, the Bonn Convention, and the many national and regional ecological networks already under development.

Restoration Area

Degraded parts of core areas, buffer zones and corridors created generally by human interventions, mainly habitat change.

Contents

Index

1 List of text boxes

2. List of tables

3. List of figures

4. List of maps

Abbreviations

BCC	Biodiversity Conservation Center (Russia)
CAP	Common Agriculture Policy
CARDS	European Community Assistance for Reconstruction Development and Stabilisation Programme
CBD	Convention on Biological Diversity
CEEC	Central and Eastern European Countries
OP	Conference of Parties
EAFRD	European Agricultural Fund for Rural Development
EAGGF	European Agricultural Guidance and Guarantee Fund
EBRI	European Biodiversity Resourcing Initiative
EC	European Commission
ECMEN	European Coastal and Marine Ecological Network
ECNC	European Centre for Nature Conservation
EEA	European Environment Agency
EECONET	European Ecological Network
ERDF	European Regional Development Fund
ETC/BD	European Topic Centre on Biological Diversity
ETF/BBB	European Task Force on Banking, Business and Biodiversity
EU	European Union
EUCC	The Coastal Union
GIS	Geographic Information System
GEF	Global Environment Facility
HELCOM	Helsinki Commission (Baltic Marine Environment Protection Commission
HNVFA	High Nature Value Farming Areas
IUCN	World Conservation Union
IVON	Integraal Verwevings-en Ondersteunend Netwerk (Flemish network)
MCPFE	Ministerial Conference on the Protection of Forests in Europe
MPA	Marine protected area
NGO	Non-governmental organisation
NIS	Newly Independent States
OSPAR	Convention and Commission for the Protection of the Marine Environment of the North-East Atlantic
PCA	Priority Conservation Areas
PEBLDS	Pan-European Biological and Landscape Diversity Strategy
PEEN	Pan-European Ecological Network
PoW	Programme of Work
RUSECONET	Russian Ecological Network
SBSTTA	Subsidiary Body on Scientific Technical and Technological Advice
SEA	Strategic environmental assessment
SICONA	Syndicat intercommunal de conservation de la nature (Luxembourg)
SPAMI	Specially protected area of Mediterranean importance
TSES	Territorial System of Ecological Stability
UNECE	United Nations Economic Commision for Europe
UNEP	United Nations Environment Programme
VEN	Vlaams Ecologisch Netwerk (Flemish ecological network)
WWF	World Wide Fund for Nature

Titles available in the various series

Nature and environment

1.   Aspects of forest management, 1968 (out of print)
2.   Freshwater, 1968 (out of print)
3.   Animals in danger, 1969 (out of print)
4.   A handbook for local authorities, 1971 (out of print)
5.   Soil conservation, 1972 (out of print)
6.   Endangered Alpine regions and disaster prevention measures, 1974 (out of print)
7.   Air pollution problems – Manual of experiments, 1975 (out of print)
8.   Evolution and conservation of hedgerow landscapes in Europe, 1975
9.   The integrated management of the European wildlife heritage, 1975 (out of print)
10.   Threatened mammals in Europe, 1976 (out of print)
11.   The effects of recreation on the ecology of natural landscapes, 1976 (out of print)
12.   Heathlands of western Europe, 1976 (out of print)
13.   The degradation of the Mediterranean maquis, 1977 (published jointly with Unesco) (out of print)
14.   List of rare, threatened and endemic plants in Europe, 1977 (out of print)
15.   Threatened amphibians and reptiles in Europe, 1978 (out of print)
16.   Vegetation map (scale 1:3 000 000) of the Council of Europe member states, 1979
17.   Model outline environmental impact statement from the standpoint of integrated management or planning of the natural environment, 1980
18.   Threatened freshwater fish of Europe, 1980
19.   European peatlands, 1980
20.   Behaviour of the public in protected areas, 1981 (out of print)
21.   Dry grasslands of Europe, 1981
22.   Alluvial forests in Europe, 1981
23.   Threatened Rhopalocera (butterflies) in Europe, 1981 (out of print)
24.   Birds in need of special protection in Europe, 1981 (out of print)
25.   Inventory and classification of marine benthic biocenoses of the Mediterranean, 1982
26.   Town farms, 1982 (out of print)
27.   List of rare, threatened and endemic plants in Europe (1982 edition), 1983
28.   Nature in cities, 1982 (out of print)
29.   The vegetation of the Alps, 1983
30.   Salt marshes in Europe, 1984 (out of print)
31.   Protected marine areas, 1985
32.   European dune and shoreline vegetation, 1985 (out of print)
33.   Ecological repercussions of constructing and using ski-runs, 1986 (out of print)
34.   Environmental education for the farming community – Experimental schemes in Europe, 1987 (2nd edition, 1994)
35.   Invertebrates in need of special protection in Europe, 1987
36.   Development of flora and fauna in urban areas, 1987 (out of print)
37.   Conservation of marine benthic biocenoses in the North Sea and the Baltic, 1987
38.   The protection of dragonflies (Odonata) and their biotopes, 1988 (out of print)
39.   Problems of soil conservation, 1988
40.   Texts adopted by the Council of Europe in the field of the conservation of European wildlife and natural habitats, 1993
41.   The biology, status and conservation of the monk seal (Monachus monachus), 1989
42.   Saproxylic invertebrates and their conservation, 1989
43.   Possible causes of forest decline and research programmes in Europe, 1989 (out of print)
44.   The biological significance and conservation of Hymenoptera in Europe, 1990
45.   Status, conservation needs and reintroduction of the lynx (Lynx lynx) in Europe, 1990
46.   Conservation of threatened freshwater fish in Europe, 1991 (2nd edition, 1994)
47.   Status and conservation needs of the wolf (Canis lupus) in the Council of Europe member states, 1990
48.   Marine turtles in the Mediterranean: distribution, population status, conservation, 1990

49. Evergreen forests in the Macaronesian Region, 1990 (out of print)
50. Marine reserves and conservation of Mediterranean coastal habitats, 1990
51. Towards the conservation of aculeate Hymenoptera in Europe, 1991
52. The means of giving greater prominence to environmental issues in agricultural education at secondary school level, 1992
53. Présentation et étude comparative de quatre réseaux de zones protégées en Europe, 1991 (available in French only)
54. The wild mink (Mustela lutreola) in Europe, 1992
55. Status and conservation of the pardel lynx (Lynx pardina) in the Iberian Peninsula, 1992
56. The conservation of natural habitats outside protected areas: legal analysis, 1992
57. The conservation of European orchids, 1992
58. Balanced development of the countryside in western Europe, 1992
59. Rehabilitation of natural habitats in rural areas, 1992
60. Datasheets of flora species – Volume I, 1992
61. Datasheets of flora species – Volume II, 1992
62. Datasheets of flora species – Volume III, 1992
63. Datasheets of flora species – Volume IV, 1992
64. Threatened non-marine molluscs of Europe, 1992
65. Potential long-term ecological impact of genetically modified organisms, 1993
66. Conservation of freshwater fish in Europe, 1994
67. Status and conservation needs of the otter (Lutra lutra) in the western Palaearctic, 1994
68. Guidelines to be followed in the design of plant conservation or recovery plans, 1994
69. Status and conservation of the wildcat (Felis silvestris) in Europe and around the Mediterranean rim, 1994
70. The integrated development of the countryside in central and eastern European countries, 1994
71. European soil resources, 1995
72. Underground habitats and their protection, 1995
73. Introduction of non-native organisms into the natural environment, 1996
74. Pan-European Biological and Landscape Diversity Strategy, 1996
75. Texts adopted by the Standing Committee of the Bern Convention on the Conservation of European Wildlife and Natural Habitats (19.IX.1979) (1982-97), 1997
76. Status and conservation of Desmaninae in Europe, 1996
77. Listing of biotopes in Europe according to their significance for invertebrates, 1996
78. A classification of Palaearctic habitats, 1996
79. Background information on invertebrates of the Habitats Directive and the Bern Convention – Part I: Crustacea, Coleoptera and Lepidoptera, 1996
80. Background information on invertebrates of the Habitats Directive and the Bern Convention – Part II: Mantodea, Orthoptera and Arachnida, 1996
81. Background information on invertebrates of the Habitats Directive and the Bern Convention – Part III: Mollusca and Echinodermata, 1996
82. Legal measures for the conservation of natural areas, 1996
83. Tourism and environment in European countries, 1996
84. Compensation for damage caused by wild animals, 1996
85. Private or voluntary systems of natural habitats' protection and management, 1996
86. Management of the beaver (Castor fiber): towards restoration of its former distribution and ecological function in Europe, 1997
87. Introduction of non-native plants into the natural environment, 1997
88. Comparative analysis of the effectiveness of legislation for the protection of wild flora in Europe, 1997
89. Legal obstacles to the application of nature conservation legislation, 1997
90. The conservation and management of the European badger (Meles meles), 1997
91. Study of biotopes and habitats losing wildlife interest as a result of ecological succession, 1997
92. Guidelines for action plans for animal species: planning recovery, 1997
93. First phase report of the Trebon otter project, 1998
94. Protection of biological and landscape diversity in agricultural landscapes of central and Eastern Europe, 1999
95. Nature conservation sites designated in application of international instruments at pan-European level, 1999

96. Progress report on the implementation of the Pan-European Biological and Landscape Diversity Strategy, 1999
97. Action plan for Maculinea butterflies in Europe, 1999
98. Environmental training for tourism professionals, 1999
99. Red Data Book of European Butterflies (Rhopalocera), (not yet issued)
100. Action Plan for Cypripedium Calceolus in Europe, 1999
101. Model law on sustainable management of coastal zones and European code of conduct for coastal zones, 1999
102. Implementation of the Bern Convention – Nordic countries: Sweden, 2000
103. Implementation of the Bern Convention – Nordic countries: Norway, 2000
104. Implementation of the Bern Convention – Nordic countries: Denmark, 2000
105. Implementation of the Bern Convention – Nordic countries: Finland, 2002 (not issued)
106. Status of hamsters Criterius criterius, Criterius migratorius, Mesocricetus newtoni and other hamster species in Europe, 2000
107. General guidelines for the development of the Pan-European Ecological Network, 2000
108. Action plan for the conservation of the pond bat in Europe (Myotis dasycneme), 2000
109. Action plan for the conservation of the greater horseshoe bat in Europe (Rhinolophus ferrumequinum), 2000
110. National and Regional Approaches for Ecological Networks in Europe, 2001
111. Action plan for the conservation of the Iberian lynx in Europe (Lynx pardinus), 2000
112. Action plan for the conservation of the Eurasian lynx in Europe (Lynx lynx), 2000
113. Action plan for the conservation of the wolves in Europe (Canis lupus), 2000
114. Action plan for the conservation of the brown bear in Europe (Ursus arctos), 2000
115. Action plan for the conservation of the wolverines in Europe (Gulo gulo), 2000
116. Tourism and the environment in European countries, 2000
117. Action plan for Margaritifera auricularia and Margaritifera margaritifera in Europe, 2001
118. Methods to control and eradicate non-native terrestrial vertebrate species, 2001
119. Texts adopted by the Standing Committee of the Convention on the Conservation of European Wildlife and Natural Habitats (Bern, 19 September 1979) (1997-2000), 2001
120. Compendium of Recommendations and Resolutions adopted by the Committee of Ministers in the field of the Environment (Russian version only) 2001
121. The micro-reserves as a tool for conservation of threatened plants in Europe (English only), 2001
122. Threatened mushrooms in Europe, 2001
123. Corridors for birds within a Pan-European Ecological Network, 2002
124. Guidelines on the application of existing international instruments in developing the Pan-European Ecological Network, 2002
125. Ecological corridors in land use planning and development policies, 2002 (English only)
126. Ecological network and local authorities – Sociological instruments, 2002
127. Ecological corridors and species – large carnivores in the Alpine region, 2002
128. Identification of the most important transboundary protected areas in Central and Eastern Europe
129. Guidelines for the constitution of ecological river networks, 2002
130. The Pan-Alpine Conservation Strategy for the Lynx, 2003
131. Code of Practice for the introduction of biological and landscape diversity considerations into the transport sector, 2003
132. Studies on transport and biological and landscape diversity, 2003
133. "High-level Pan-European Conference on Agriculture and Biodiversity" – Compendium of background reports, 2003
134. Corridors and ecosystems: coastal and marine areas, 2003 (English only)
135. The restoration of sites and ecological corridors in the framework of building up a Pan-European Ecological Network, with examples of best practices from European countries, 2003 (English only)
136. 33 threatened fungi in Europe, 2004 (English only)
137. European strategy on invasive alien species, 2004
138. The implementation of the Bern Convention in Ireland, 2004 (English only)
139. Windfarms and birds, 2004 (English only)
140. Protecting birds from powerlines, 2004 (English only)
141. European bison (Bison bonasus) – Current state of the species and action plan for its

conservation, 2004 (English only)
142. Texts adopted by the Standing Committee of the Convention on the Conservation of European Wildlife and Natural Habitats (Berne, 19 September 1979) 2001-2004, 2005
143. Using tax incentives to conserve and enhance biodiversity in Europe, 2005
144. Action Plan for the conservation of sturgeons (Acipenseridae) in the Danube River Basin, 2006
145. European Strategy for the conservation of invertebrates, 2007
146. The Pan-European Ecological Network: taking stock, 2007
147. The implementation of the Bern Convention in Hungary, 2007
148. The implementation of the Bern Convention in Spain, 2007
149. Conserving European Biodiversity in the context of climate change, 2007

Environmental encounters
1. Environmental training in agricultural circles, 1987 (out of print)
2. Parks, plans and people – Protected areas and socio-economic development, 1987 (out of print)
3. Workshop on the situation and protection of ancient natural and semi-natural woodlands in Europe, 1987
4. A new management of the environment in rural areas, 1988
5. Training course for managers of protected areas in Europe and Africa, 1989
6. The situation of the brown bear (Ursus arctos) in Europe, 1989
7. Nature tomorrow, 1989
8. The conservation of wild progenitors of cultivated plants, 1991
9. Nature museums: tools for learning about, promoting and protecting the natural heritage of Europe, 1990
10. Colloquy on the Bern Convention invertebrates and their conservation, 1990 (out of print)
11. The situation, conservation needs and reintroduction of the lynx in Europe, 1992
12. The management of Mediterranean wetlands, 1992
13. The conservation of the Mediterranean monk seal, 1992
14. Wetland invertebrates, 1992
15. Seminar for managers of diploma-holding areas, 1992
16. Seminar on the biology and conservation of the wildcat (Felis silvestris) (Bilingual edition), 1993
17. Seminar on the management of small populations of threatened mammals, 1994
18. Workshop on nature conservation in central and eastern Europe, 1994
19. Seminar on recovery plans for species of amphibians and reptiles, 1994
20. Pan-European conference on the potential long-term ecological impact of genetically modified organisms, 1995
21. Between the two extremes – dereliction and over-use: how shall the land be managed so as to benefit the wildlife, the countryside and the landscape?, 1995
22. Symposium on the United Nations Conference on Environment and Development (UNCED), the Convention on Biological Diversity and the Bern Convention: the next steps, 1995
23. Protection of coastal areas of the Adriatic Sea, 1995
24. Seminar on the conservation of the European otter (Lutra lutra), 1996
25. Seminar on the biology and conservation of European desmans and water shrews (Galemys pyrenaicus, Desmana moschata, Neomys spp.), 1996
26. Landscape diversity: A chance for the rural community to achieve a sustainable future, 1996
27. How hunting and fishing can contribute to nature conservation and rural development (bilingual edition), 1996
28. Seminar for managers of diploma-holding areas, 1996
29. Environmental education, 1996
30. Environmental education in school systems, 1996
31. Agriculture and related activities in protected areas, 1996
32. Sustainable tourism development, 1996
33. Colloquy on conservation, management and restoration of habitats for invertebrates: enhancing biological diversity, 1997

34. Colloquy on sustainable tourism development: reconciling economic, cultural, social, scientific and environmental factors, 1997
35. Seminar on incentive measures for the voluntary creation and management of protected areas, 1997 (bilingual edition)
36. Tourism and environment: towards a new tourist culture, 1998
37. Environment conservation and the media, 1998
38. The re-introduction of the Lynx into the Alps, 1998
39. Drafting and implementing action plans for threatened species, 1998
40. Protected areas: centres for propagating a general nature conservation policy, 1998
41. Links between the sustainable development of tourism and regional/spatial planning, 1999
42 The Bern Convention and national case law: effecting implementation, 2000
43. Tourism and environment: the natural, cultural and socio-economic challenges of sustainable tourism, 2000
44. 1st international symposium of the Pan-European Ecological Network: "Nature does not have any borders: towards transfrontier ecological networks", 2000
45. Workshop on Ecological corridors for invertebrates: strategies of dispersal and recolonisation in today's agricultural and forestry landscapes, 2001
46. Communication and biodiversity, 2001
47. Nature as heritage: from awareness to action, 2002
48. International Colloquy in tribute to the memory of Cyrille de Klemm: "Biological diversity and environmental law", 2001
49. Biological and landscape diversity in Ukraine, 2001
50. The partnership of local and regional authorities in the conservation of biological and landscape diversity, 2001
51. Sustainable tourism, environment and employment, 2002
52. Awareness to the landscape: from perception to protection, 2002
53. High-level Pan-European Conference on Agriculture and Biodiversity: towards integrating biological and landscape diversity for sustainable agriculture in Europe, 2003
54. 3rd International Symposium of the Pan-European Ecological Network "Fragmentation of habitats and ecological corridors", 2003
55. Marine and coastal ecological corridors, 2003
56. 4th International Symposium of the Pan-European Ecological Network "Marine and coastal biodiversity and protected areas", 2004
57. 5th International Symposium of the Pan-European Ecological Network "Pan-European Ecological Network in forests: conservation of biodiversity and sustainable management", 2005
58. 2nd Confernce on the Status and Conservation of the Alpine Lynx (SCALP), 2005 (Amden, Switzerland, 7-9 May 2003) (English only)
59. Invasive plants in Mediterranean regions of the world, 2006
60. Transboundary management of large carnivore populations, 2006
61. The 25th anniversary of the Bern Convention
62. 40th anniversary of the European Diploma – A network for nature and people

Questions & Answers

1. Biodiversity, 1997
2. Agriculture and biodiversity, 1997
3. Tourism and environment, 1998
4. The pan-European ecological network, 1998
5. Forests and biodiversity, 1999
6. The European diploma for protected areas, 2000
7. Integration of biodiversity into sectoral policies, 2003
8. Conservation of large carnivores in Europe, 2005
9. The Bern Convention, 2007

Planning and management
1.   Hedges, 1988
2.   Farming and wildlife, 1989
3.   Watercourses. Conservation, maintenance and management, 1994
4.   Rural landscapes in Europe: principles for creation and management, 1994
5.   Amphibians and reptiles: conservation management of species and habitats, 1997

Other publications

Naturopa journal (3 issues per year, in English and French)

Management of Europe's natural heritage – twenty-five years of activity, 1987 (out of print)

A European cultural revolution: the Council of Europe's "Charter of invertebrates", 1986 (out of print)

The Bern Convention on Nature Conservation, 1991

Contribution to the United Nations Conference on Environment and Development (UNCED), 1993

European conservation strategy, 1993

The state of the environment in Europe: the scientists take stock of the situation, 1993

Model law on the protection of the environment, 1994

The Council of Europe and the protection of the environment, 1995

The Council of Europe and the environment, 2002

Texts adopted by the Council of Europe in the field of the environment, 2002 (bilingual edition)

The majority of the Council of Europe's publications are available in English and French editions.

Sales agents for publications of the Council of Europe
Agents de vente des publications du Conseil de l'Europe

BELGIUM/BELGIQUE
La Librairie Européenne -
The European Bookshop
Rue de l'Orme, 1
B-1040 BRUXELLES
Tel.: +32 (0)2 231 04 35
Fax: +32 (0)2 735 08 60
E-mail: order@libeurop.be
http://www.libeurop.be

Jean De Lannoy
Avenue du Roi 202 Koningslaan
B-1190 BRUXELLES
Tel.: +32 (0)2 538 43 08
Fax: +32 (0)2 538 08 41
E-mail: jean.de.lannoy@dl-servi.com
http://www.jean-de-lannoy.be

CANADA
Renouf Publishing Co. Ltd.
1-5369 Canotek Road
OTTAWA, Ontario K1J 9J3, Canada
Tel.: +1 613 745 2665
Fax: +1 613 745 7660
Toll-Free Tel.: (866) 767-6766
E-mail: order.dept@renoufbooks.com
http://www.renoufbooks.com

CZECH REPUBLIC/
RÉPUBLIQUE TCHÈQUE
Suweco CZ, s.r.o.
Klecakova 347
CZ-180 21 PRAHA 9
Tel.: +420 2 424 59 204
Fax: +420 2 848 21 646
E-mail: import@suweco.cz
http://www.suweco.cz

DENMARK/DANEMARK
GAD
Vimmelskaftet 32
DK-1161 KØBENHAVN K
Tel.: +45 77 66 60 00
Fax: +45 77 66 60 01
E-mail: gad@gad.dk
http://www.gad.dk

FINLAND/FINLANDE
Akateeminen Kirjakauppa
PO Box 128
Keskuskatu 1
FIN-00100 HELSINKI
Tel.: +358 (0)9 121 4430
Fax: +358 (0)9 121 4242
E-mail: akatilaus@akateeminen.com
http://www.akateeminen.com

FRANCE
La Documentation française
(diffusion/distribution France entière)
124, rue Henri Barbusse
F-93308 AUBERVILLIERS CEDEX
Tél.: +33 (0)1 40 15 70 00
Fax: +33 (0)1 40 15 68 00
E-mail: commande@ladocumentationfrancaise.fr
http://www.ladocumentationfrancaise.fr

Librairie Kléber
1 rue des Francs Bourgeois
F-67000 STRASBOURG
Tel.: +33 (0)3 88 15 78 88
Fax: +33 (0)3 88 15 78 80
E-mail: francois.wolfermann@librairie-kleber.fr
http://www.librairie-kleber.com

GERMANY/ALLEMAGNE
AUSTRIA/AUTRICHE
UNO Verlag GmbH
August-Bebel-Allee 6
D-53175 BONN
Tel.: +49 (0)228 94 90 20
Fax: +49 (0)228 94 90 222
E-mail: bestellung@uno-verlag.de
http://www.uno-verlag.de

GREECE/GRÈCE
Librairie Kauffmann s.a.
Stadiou 28
GR-105 64 ATHINAI
Tel.: +30 210 32 55 321
Fax.: +30 210 32 30 320
E-mail: ord@otenet.gr
http://www.kauffmann.gr

HUNGARY/HONGRIE
Euro Info Service kft.
1137 Bp. Szent István krt. 12.
H-1137 BUDAPEST
Tel.: +36 (06)1 329 2170
Fax: +36 (06)1 349 2053
E-mail: euroinfo@euroinfo.hu
http://www.euroinfo.hu

ITALY/ITALIE
Licosa SpA
Via Duca di Calabria, 1/1
I-50125 FIRENZE
Tel.: +39 0556 483215
Fax: +39 0556 41257
E-mail: licosa@licosa.com
http://www.licosa.com

MEXICO/MEXIQUE
Mundi-Prensa México, S.A. De C.V.
Río Pánuco, 141 Delegacíon Cuauhtémoc
06500 MÉXICO, D.F.
Tel.: +52 (01)55 55 33 56 58
Fax: +52 (01)55 55 14 67 99
E-mail: mundiprensa@mundiprensa.com.mx
http://www.mundiprensa.com.mx

NETHERLANDS/PAYS-BAS
De Lindeboom Internationale Publicaties b.v.
M.A. de Ruyterstraat 20 A
NL-7482 BZ HAAKSBERGEN
Tel.: +31 (0)53 5740004
Fax: +31 (0)53 5729296
E-mail: books@delindeboom.com
http://www.delindeboom.com

NORWAY/NORVÈGE
Akademika
Postboks 84 Blindern
N-0314 OSLO
Tel.: +47 2 218 8100
Fax: +47 2 218 8103
E-mail: support@akademika.no
http://www.akademika.no

POLAND/POLOGNE
Ars Polona JSC
25 Obroncow Street
PL-03-933 WARSZAWA
Tel.: +48 (0)22 509 86 00
Fax: +48 (0)22 509 86 10
E-mail: arspolona@arspolona.com.pl
http://www.arspolona.com.pl

PORTUGAL
Livraria Portugal
(Dias & Andrade, Lda.)
Rua do Carmo, 70
P-1200-094 LISBOA
Tel.: +351 21 347 42 82 / 85
Fax: +351 21 347 02 64
E-mail: info@livrariaportugal.pt
http://www.livrariaportugal.pt

RUSSIAN FEDERATION/
FÉDÉRATION DE RUSSIE
Ves Mir
9a, Kolpacnhyi per.
RU-101000 MOSCOW
Tel.: +7 (8)495 623 6839
Fax: +7 (8)495 625 4269
E-mail: orders@vesmirbooks.ru
http://www.vesmirbooks.ru

SPAIN/ESPAGNE
Mundi-Prensa Libros, s.a.
Castelló, 37
E-28001 MADRID
Tel.: +34 914 36 37 00
Fax: +34 915 75 39 98
E-mail: libreria@mundiprensa.es
http://www.mundiprensa.com

SWITZERLAND/SUISSE
Van Diermen Editions – ADECO
Chemin du Lacuez 41
CH-1807 BLONAY
Tel.: +41 (0)21 943 26 73
Fax: +41 (0)21 943 36 05
E-mail: info@adeco.org
http://www.adeco.org

UNITED KINGDOM/ROYAUME-UNI
The Stationery Office Ltd
PO Box 29
GB-NORWICH NR3 1GN
Tel.: +44 (0)870 600 5522
Fax: +44 (0)870 600 5533
E-mail: book.enquiries@tso.co.uk
http://www.tsoshop.co.uk

UNITED STATES and CANADA/
ÉTATS-UNIS et CANADA
Manhattan Publishing Company
468 Albany Post Road
CROTTON-ON-HUDSON, NY 10520, USA
Tel.: +1 914 271 5194
Fax: +1 914 271 5856
E-mail: Info@manhattanpublishing.com
http://www.manhattanpublishing.com

Council of Europe Publishing/Editions du Conseil de l'Europe
F-67075 Strasbourg Cedex
Tel.: +33 (0)3 88 41 25 81 – Fax: +33 (0)3 88 41 39 10 – E-mail: publishing@coe.int – Website: http://book.coe.int